Anthems
Old &
New
for Upper Voices

**100 settings selected
by Kevin Mayhew**

VOLUME ONE

Kevin
Mayhew

We hope you enjoy *Anthems Old & New for Upper Voices, Volume 1.*
Further copies are available from your local Kevin Mayhew stockist.

In case of difficulty, please contact the publisher direct by writing to:

The Sales Department
KEVIN MAYHEW LTD
Buxhall
Stowmarket
Suffolk IP14 3BW

Phone 01449 737978
Fax 01449 737834
E-mail info@kevinmayhewltd.com

Please ask for our complete catalogue of outstanding Church Music.

First published in Great Britain in 2001 by Kevin Mayhew Ltd.

© Copyright 2001 Kevin Mayhew Ltd.

ISBN 1 84003 705 9
ISMN M 57004 836 6
Catalogue No: 1450214

0 1 2 3 4 5 6 7 8 9

Cover design by Jonathan Stroulger

Music setter: Kate Gallaher
Proof reader: Linda Ottewell

Printed and bound in Great Britain

CONTENTS

Page no.

And the glory of the Lord	George Frideric Handel	8
A new commandment	Malcolm Archer	16
A song of creation	Malcolm Archer	20
As the deer pants for the water	Martin Nystrom	24
As the deer that thirsts	Colin Mawby	30
Ave Maria	Jacob Arcadelt	32
Ave Maria	Johann Sebastian Bach/Charles Gounod	35
Ave Maria	Colin Mawby	43
Ave Maria	Giulio Caccini	46
Ave verum corpus	Wolfgang Amadeus Mozart	52
Ave verum corpus	Malcolm Archer	56
Behold, the Lord will come!	Colin Mawby	62
Benedic anima mea Domino	George Malcolm	65
Be still, for the presence of the Lord	David J. Evans	67
Brightest and best	Malcolm Archer	70
Calm me, Lord	Margaret Rizza	76
Christ be with me	Johann Pachelbel	78
Christ the Lord is risen again	Richard Lloyd	82
Come and bring your gifts	Richard Shephard	87
Come, Holy Ghost	Thomas Attwood	90
Come, let us all this day	Johann Sebastian Bach	96
Come on and celebrate	Dave Bankhead/Patricia Morgan	100
Come, prepare the way	Jeremiah Clarke	107
Come, Spirit of our God	Alan Rees	112
Come to me	Margaret Rizza	115
Desiderium animae	George Malcolm	121
Give thanks to the Lord our God	Richard Lloyd	122
Gladness, sadness, joy and sorrow	Edward MacDowell	127
God is good	Graham Kendrick	130
God so loved the world	John Stainer	134

God who made the earth	Malcolm Archer	140
Great indeed are your works, O Lord	Aniceto Nazareth	144
Haec dies	Colin Mawby	146
Hallelujah Chorus	George Frideric Handel	149
He shall feed his flock	George Frideric Handel	160
Holy God	Kevin Mayhew	165
Holy Spirit, truth divine	Alan Viner	166
Hymn to the Holy Spirit	Malcolm Archer	170
I call on thee, Lord Jesus Christ	Stanley Vann	174
If anyone loves me	Andrew Moore	178
If with all your hearts	Felix Mendelssohn	181
I will be with you	Gerard Markland	184
I will lift up mine eyes	Noel Rawsthorne	187
I will magnify thee, O Lord	Joseph Corfe	190
Jesu, joy of our desiring	Johann Sebastian Bach	196
Jesus, you are the way	Margaret Rizza	202
Jesus, you died for me	Wolfgang Amadeus Mozart	208
Laudate Dominum	Giuseppe Ottavio Pitoni	211
Laudate Dominum	Wolfgang Amadeus Mozart	216
Lead, kindly light	Malcolm Archer	224
Lead me, Lord	Samuel Sebastian Wesley	229
Let all the world in every corner sing	Malcolm Archer	232
Let love be real	Christopher Tambling	237
Let our praise to you	Malcolm Archer	240
Lift up your heads, O ye gates	George Frideric Handel	243
Listen	Aniceto Nazareth	252
Lord, I lift my hands to you	Ludwig van Beethoven	255
Lord, you have touched my life	Ludwig van Beethoven	258
Love the Lord	Andrew Moore	263
Magnificat	Kevin Mayhew	268
May the Lord bless you	Margaret Rizza	270
Morning has broken	Traditional Gaelic melody	272
O eternal God	Kevin Mayhew	274
O for the wings of a dove	Felix Mendelssohn	278
O Lord, my heart is not proud	Margaret Rizza	282

O love, I give myself to thee	William Lloyd Webber	284
O sing unto the Lord	Noel Rawsthorne	292
Panis angelicus	César Franck	294
Peace, perfect peace	Kevin Mayhew	299
Pie Jesu	Gabriel Fauré	304
Praise our God	Andrew Moore	308
Praise to the Lord	Richard Lloyd	312
Praise to the Lord, the Almighty	Malcolm Archer	318
Proclaim the story	Marc-Antoine Charpentier	326
Save us, O Lord	Kevin Mayhew	331
Send forth your Spirit	Margaret Rizza	332
Send forth your Spirit, O Lord	Aniceto Nazareth	334
Silent, surrendered	Margaret Rizza	336
Sing aloud, the day is breaking	Ludwig van Beethoven	338
Sing, Holy Mother	Kevin Mayhew	344
Sing praise and thanksgiving	Malcolm Archer	346
Sing to the Lord	Franz Schubert	352
Softly, tread softly	Kevin Mayhew	355
Song for a young prophet	Damian Lundy	360
Sound out his praises!	George Frideric Handel	362
Take my hands, Lord	Margaret Rizza	366
The body of Christ is broken	Rosalie Bonighton	369
The Grail Prayer	Margaret Rizza	374
The heavens are telling	Franz Joseph Haydn	380
The Lord comes down from heaven	Andrew Moore	389
The Spirit lives to set us free	Damian Lundy	392
To be in your presence	Noel Richards	398
Veni, lumen cordium	Margaret Rizza	402
Wake up, O people	Marie Lydia Pereira	404
We are his people	Andrew Moore	406
What kind of man was this	Christopher Tambling	408
When I survey the wondrous cross	Malcolm Archer	412
Wonderful your deeds, Lord	Adrian Vernon Fish	416
You are the centre	Margaret Rizza	419
Zadok the priest	George Frideric Handel	422

Index of Uses

Adoration

	Page no.
As the deer pants for the water	24
As the deer that thirsts	30

Advent

Come, prepare the way	107
Wake up, O people	404

Baptism

Be still, for the presence of the Lord	67
Hymn to the Holy Spirit	170
Silent, surrendered	336
Song for a young prophet	360

Blessed Virgin Mary

Ave Maria (Arcadelt)	32
Ave Maria (Bach/Gounod)	35
Ave Maria (Mawby)	43
Ave Maria (Caccini)	46
Sing, Holy Mother	344

Christ the King

Desiderium animae	121
Let all the world in every corner sing	232
Lift up your heads, O ye gates	243
Proclaim the story	326
Sing to the Lord	352

Christmas

Brightest and best	70

Communion

Ave verum corpus (Mozart)	52
Ave verum corpus (Archer)	56
O eternal God	274
Panis angelicus	294
The body of Christ is broken	369

Confidence

And the glory of the Lord	8
Behold, the Lord will come!	62
Christ be with me	78
Come to me	115
He shall feed his flock	160
If with all your hearts	181
I will be with you	184
I will lift up mine eyes	187
Jesus, you are the way	202
Lead me, Lord	229
Let love be real	237
Softly, tread softly	355

Confirmation

Be still, for the presence of the Lord	67

Come, Holy Ghost / continued

Come, Holy Ghost	90
Holy Spirit, truth divine	166
Hymn to the Holy Spirit	170
Silent, surrendered	336

Coronation

Desiderium animae	121
Zadok the priest	422

Corpus Christi

Ave verum corpus (Mozart)	52
Ave verum corpus (Archer)	56

Dedication

As the deer that thirsts	30
Christ be with me	78
Holy God	165
I call on thee, Lord Jesus Christ	174
If anyone loves me	178
I will be with you	184
Lead me, Lord	229
O love, I give myself to thee	284
Softly, tread softly	355
Take my hands, Lord	366
The Grail Prayer	374
To be in your presence	398
You are the centre	419

Easter

Christ the Lord is risen again	82
Haec dies	146
Hallelujah Chorus	149

Funeral

He shall feed his flock	160
Pie Jesu	304

Justice

Magnificat	268
Take my hands, Lord	366
The Lord comes down from heaven	389

Marriage

Jesu, joy of our desiring	196
O for the wings of a dove	278

Morning

Morning has broken	272
Sing aloud, the day is breaking	338
The heavens are telling	380

Night

Lead, kindly light	224
Save us, O Lord	331

Opening

Come and bring your gifts	87
Come on and celebrate	100

Passiontide

Ave verum corpus (Mozart)	52
Ave verum corpus (Archer)	56
God so loved the world	134
Jesus, you died for me	208
What kind of man was this	408
When I survey the wondrous cross	412

Peace

A new commandment	16
Calm me, Lord	76
Come to me	115
Holy God	165
Jesus, you are the way	202
Lord, I lift my hands to you	255
Lord, you have touched me life	258
Love the Lord	263
O Lord, my heart is not proud	282
Peace, perfect peace	299

Penitential Service

Gladness, sadness, joy and sorrow	127
Jesus, you died for me	208

Praise

A song of creation	20
Behold, the Lord will come!	62
Benedic anima mea Domino	65
Come and bring your gifts	87
Come on and celebrate	100
Give thanks to the Lord our God	122
God is good	130
God who made the earth	140
Great indeed are your works, O Lord	144
Haec dies	146
Hallelujah Chorus	149
I will magnify thee, O Lord	190
Laudate Dominum (Pitoni)	211
Laudate Dominum (Mozart)	216
Let all the world in every corner sing	232
Let our praise to you	240
O sing unto the Lord	292
Praise our God	308
Praise to the Lord	312
Praise to the Lord, the Almighty	318
Proclaim the story	326
Send forth your Spirit	332
Send forth your Spirit, O Lord	334
Sing praise and thanksgiving	346
Sing to the Lord	352
Sound out his praises!	362

The heavens are telling	380
The Lord comes down from heaven	389
We are his people	406
Wonderful your deeds, Lord	416
Zadok the priest	422

Prayer

Be still, for the presence of the Lord	67
Calm me, Lord	76
Holy God	165
I call on thee, Lord Jesus Christ	174
Lord, I lift my hands to you	255
May the Lord bless you	270
O eternal God	274
O Lord, my heart is not proud	282
Peace, perfect peace	299

Thanksgiving

A song of creation	20
Benedic anima mea Domino	65
Come on and celebrate	100
Give thanks to the Lord our God	122
God is good	130
Great indeed are your works, O Lord	144
Laudate Dominum (Pitoni)	211
Laudate Dominum (Mozart)	216
Let all the world in every corner sing	232
Lord, you have touched my life	258
Send forth your Spirit	332
Send forth your Spirit, O Lord	334
Sing praise and thanksgiving	346
Sound out his praises!	362
We are his people	406

Trinity

A song of creation	20

Unity

Magnificat	268
The Spirit lives to set us free	392

Whitsun

A new commandment	16
Come, Holy Ghost	90
Come, let us all this day	96
Come, Spirit of our God	112
Holy Spirit, truth divine	166
Hymn to the Holy Spirit	170
Listen	252
Silent, surrendered	336
The Spirit lives to set us free	392
Veni, lumen cordium	402

AND THE GLORY OF THE LORD

Text: from Scripture
Music: George Frideric Handel (1685-1759) arr. Colin Hand

Where the text '-ry of' is to be sung to one note, the two syllables should be run together.

glo - ry, the glo - ry of the Lord shall be re - vea - led,

glo - ry, the glo - ry of the Lord shall be re - vea - led,

and all flesh shall

Man.

and all flesh shall see it to -

see it to - ge - ther,

Ped.   Man.

10

* *div. if practicable, otherwise take upper notes.*

11

67
ge - ther, and all flesh shall see it to - ge -

see it to - ge - ther, and all flesh shall see it to - ge -

Ped.

73
ther, and the glo - ry, the glo - ry of the

ther, and the glo - ry, the glo - ry of the

79
Lord, and all flesh shall see it to - ge - ther, the mouth

Lord, and all flesh shall see it to - ge - ther, and the

Man.

85

of the Lord hath spo-ken it, and all flesh

glo-ry, the glo-ry of the Lord shall be re - vea-led, and all

91

and all flesh for the mouth of the Lord hath

flesh shall see it to-ge-ther, the glo-ry, the glo-ry of the

97

spo-ken it, the Lord hath spo - ken it,

Lord shall be re - veal'd, shall be re - vea - led, and all

Ped.

Man.

13

A NEW COMMANDMENT

Text: Susan Sayers (b.1946) based on John 13
Music: Malcolm Archer (b.1952)

ceive   if you love   one a - no - ther as I   love   you.

A few voices *mf*

A   new com - mand - ment I   give you   now

Choir *mf*

A   new com - mand   -   ment I   give you   now   that you

mf

that you love   one a - no   -   ther   as I have loved

love   one a - no   -   ther   as I have loved you.   By

you. You are my friends

this will all peo - ple know you are my friends

if you love as I love you.

if you love one a - no - ther as I love you.

p

Choir and Congregation

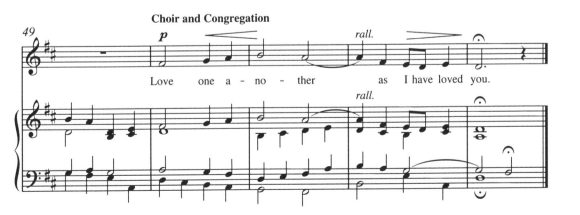

Love one a - no - ther as I have loved you.

rall.

19

A SONG OF CREATION

Text: Adapted from the Alternative Service Book
Music: Malcolm Archer (b.1952)

praise and ex - alt him for e - ver. Bless the Lord, you an - gels of the

Lord, bless the Lord, all you his hosts. Bless the

Lord, all peo - ple on earth, sing his praise and ex - alt him for

div. mf

e - ver. All men and wo - men, bless the Lord: bless the

mf

23

Lord, you priests of the Lord. *cresc.* Bless the Lord, you ser-vants of the

Lord: sing his praise and ex-alt him for e - ver. *f* Bless the

Altos

29 *f*

Ah

Lord, all you of up-right spi - rit, and you that are ho - ly and hum - ble in

heart. Bless the Fa – ther, Son and Ho - ly Spi - rit; sing his

praise and ex - alt him for e – ver.

Man.

A – men,

A – men.

Ped.

23

AS THE DEER PANTS FOR THE WATER

Text and Music: Martin Nystrom (b.1956)
arr. Christopher Tambling

You a - lone are my long to wor - ship you.

strength, my shield, to you a - lone may my spi - rit yield.

Ped.

You a - lone are my heart's de - sire and I long to wor - ship

25

ap - ple of my eye.   You   a - lone   are   my

strength, my shield,   to   you   a - lone   may   my   spi - rit   yield.

Ped.

You   a - lone   are   my   heart's   de - sire   and   I   long   to   wor - ship

you.

Man.

Sopranos and Altos

You're my friend and you're my bro-ther, e - ven though you are a

king. I love you more than a - ny o-ther, so much

more than a - ny - thing. Ah,

more than a - ny - thing. You a - lone are my strength, my shield, to

Ped.

ah,

you a - lone may my spi - rit yield. You a - lone are my

molto rit.

and I long to wor - ship you.

heart's de - sire and I long to wor - ship you.

molto rit.

AS THE DEER THAT THIRSTS

Text: Psalm 42: 1-2
Music: Colin Mawby (b.1936)

AVE MARIA

Text: Luke 1
Music: Jacob Arcadelt (1505-1568) arr. Colin Hand

AVE MARIA

Text: Luke 1
Music: adapted from Johann Sebastian Bach (1685-1750)
by Charles Gounod (1818-1893) arr. Colin Hand

Anthems

AVE MARIA

Text: Luke 1
Music: Colin Mawby (b.1936)

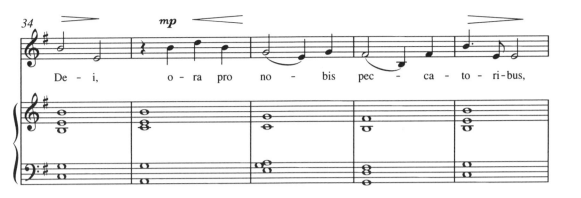

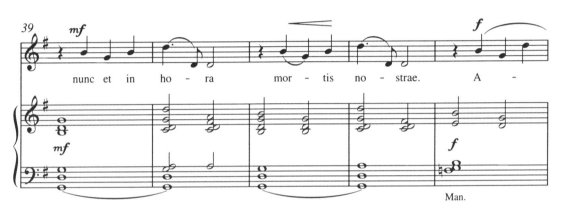

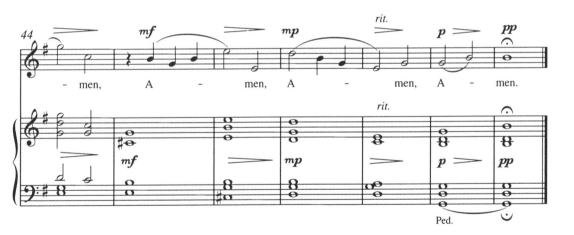

Translation: Hail Mary, full of grace, the Lord is with thee, hail Mary:
blessed art thou, blessed art thou among women,
and blessed is the fruit of thy womb, Jesus.
Holy Mary, pray, pray for us. Amen.

AVE MARIA

Text: Luke 1
Music: Giulio Caccini (c.1545-1618)
arr. Christopher Tambling

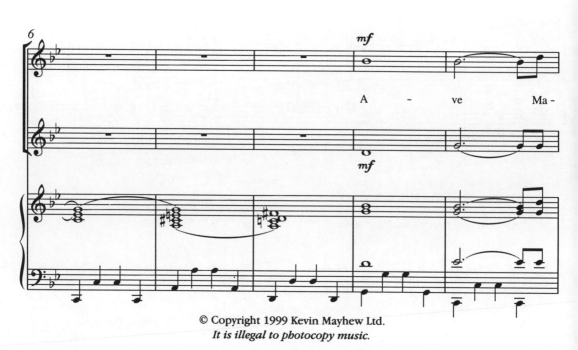

ve.

ve   Ma - ri - a,

A - - -

- - ve.

AVE VERUM CORPUS

Text: 14th Century
Music: Wolfgang Amadeus Mozart (1756-1791) arr. Alan Ridout

Translation: Hail, true body born of the Virgin Mary which truly suffered and was sacrificed on the cross for the human race, whose pierced side poured with water and blood: be to us a foretaste of the verdict to be passed at death.

AVE VERUM CORPUS

Text: Innocent VI (d.1362)
Music: Malcolm Archer (b.1952)

Translation: *Hail, true body born of the virgin Mary;*
truly suffering and sacrificed on the cross for mankind.
You, whose pierced side yielded true blood,
be our food in the trials of death.

im - mo - la - tum in cru - ce pro ho - mi - ne, ho - mi - ne.

Sopranos and Altos

A - ve, a - ve ve - rum cor - pus

na - tum ex Ma - ri - a vir - gi - ne,

ve – re pas – sum im – mo – la – tum

in cru – ce pro ho – mi – ne, ho – mi – ne.

Altos
mf

Cu – jus la – tus per – fo – ra – tum ve – ro

flu – xit san – gui – ne, es – to no – bis

Anthems

BEHOLD, THE LORD WILL COME!

Text: Michael Forster (b.1946)
Music: Colin Mawby (b.1936)

Be - hold, the Lord will come! Pre - pare the de - sert

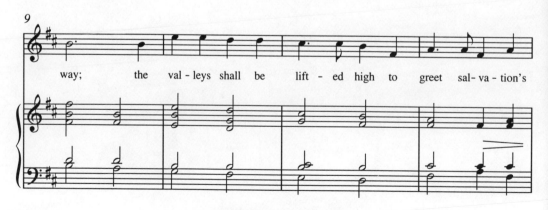

way; the val - leys shall be lift - ed high to greet sal - va - tion's

Optional Descant

What joy-ous task is ours, to he-rald and ac-claim the

vealed. What joy-ous task is ours, to he-rald and ac-claim the

co-ming of the liv-ing Lord, of high e-ter-nal name, of

co-ming of the liv-ing Lord, of high e-ter-nal name, of

high e-ter-nal name!

high e-ter-nal name!

BENEDIC ANIMA MEA DOMINO

Text: Psalm 102:2
Music: George Malcolm (1917-1998)

Translation: Bless the Lord, my soul,
and do not forget all he has given you,
and your youth will be renewed
like that of the eagle.

Anthems

BE STILL, FOR THE PRESENCE OF THE LORD

Text: David J. Evans (b.1957)
Music: David J. Evans arr. Christopher Tambling

re - ve - rence and fear. In him no
mi - ni - ster his grace. No work too

sin is found, we stand on ho - ly ground. Be still, for the
hard for him, in faith re - ceive from him. Be still, for the

Last time rit. *Fine*

pre - sence of the Lord, the Ho - ly One, is here.
pow - er of the Lord is mov - ing in this place.

Last time rit. *Fine*

(unaccompanied)

S *f*

2. Be still, for the glo - ry of the Lord is shi - ning all a -

A *f*

BRIGHTEST AND BEST

Text: Reginald Heber (1783-1826)
Music: Malcolm Archer (b.1952)

star of the east, the ho - ri - zon a - dorn - ing,
an - gels a - dore him in slum - ber re - clin - ing,

1.
guide where our in - fant Re - deem - er is laid.
Ma - ker and Mon - arch and Sa - viour of

2.
mp
all. Say, shall we yield him in cost - ly de -
mp

vo - tion, o - dours of E - dom, and off - 'rings di -

vine,   gems   of the   moun - tain,   and   pearls   of the

o - cean,   myrrh   from the   for - est,   or   gold   from   the

mine?   Vain - ly we   of - fer   each   am - ple   ob -

Ah,

Optional lower voices *p*

Sw. *mp*

ah,

star of the east, the ho – ri – zon a – dorn – ing,

ah,

guide where our in – fant Re – deem – er is laid.

p

ah.

Solo *p*

Guide where our in – fant Re – deem – er is laid.

Sw. *p*

CALM ME, LORD

Text: David Adam
Music: Margaret Rizza (b.1929)

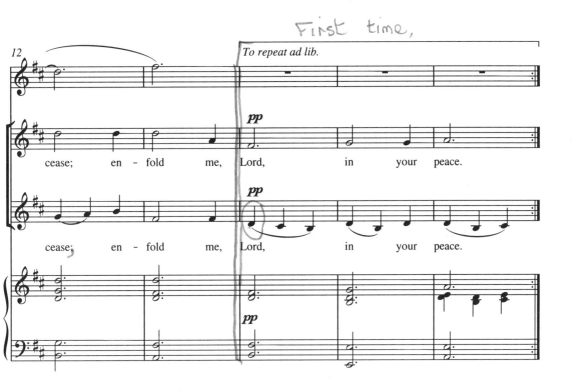

First time,

second time.

CHRIST BE WITH ME

Text: ascribed to St Patrick, trans. Cecil Frances Alexander (1818-1895)
Music: Canon in D (Johann Pachelbel)
arr. Noel Rawsthorne

Christ be with me, Christ with - in me, Christ be-hind me, Christ be-fore me,

Christ be - side me, Christ to guide me, Christ to com-fort and re - store me.

Christ be with me, Christ with - in me, Christ be - hind me, Christ be - fore me,

Christ be with me, Christ with - in me, Christ be - hind me, Christ be - fore me,

Christ be - side me, Christ to guide me, Christ to com - fort and re - store me.

Christ be - side me, Christ to guide me, Christ to com - fort and re - store me.

Christ be - neath me, Christ a - bove me, Christ in qui - et, Christ in dan - ger,

Anthems

For Michael Willams, MBE, and the girls of St John's, Buxton.

CHRIST THE LORD IS RISEN AGAIN

Text: Michael Weisse (c.1480-1534) trans. Catherine Winkworth (1827-1878) alt.
Music: Richard Lloyd (b.1933)

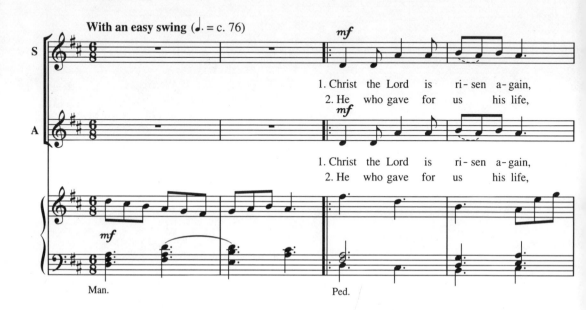

al - le - lu - ia, al - le - lu - ia!
Hark, an - ge - lic voi - ces cry,
is our pas - chal Lamb to - day,

Man.

cresc.

al - le - lu - ia, al - le - lu - ia!
Sing - ing e - ver - more on high,
We, too, sing for joy, and say,

cresc.

cresc.

Ped.

al - le - lu - ia, al - le - lu - ia!
Al - le - lu - ia, al - le - lu - ia!

83

3. He who slum - ber'd in the grave,
al - le - lu - ia, al - le - lu - ia! is ex - alt - ed now to save,
al - le - lu - ia, al - le - lu - ia! now through Christ - en - dom it rings,

al - le - lu - ia, al - le - lu - ia! that the Lamb is King of kings,

al - le - lu - ia, al - le - lu - ia! that the Lamb is King of kings,

al - le - lu - ia, al - le - lu - ia! Al - le - lu - ia, al - le - lu - ia!

al - le - lu - ia, al - le - lu - ia! Al - le - lu - ia, al - le - lu - ia!

Al - le - lu - ia, al - le - lu - ia!

Al - le - lu - ia, al - le - lu - ia!

Anthems

COME AND BRING YOUR GIFTS

Text: Hubert J. Richards (b.1921)
Music: Richard Shephard (b.1949)

Solo

Come and bring your gifts to the Lord.

4 Choir and Congregation

Come and bring your gifts to the Lord.

Solo

Our help is in the name of the

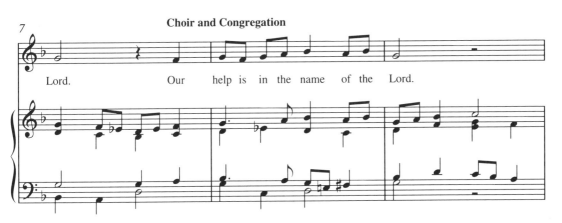

7 Choir and Congregation

Lord. Our help is in the name of the Lord.

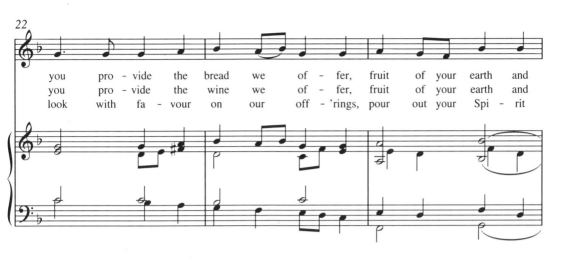

you pro - vide the bread we of - fer, fruit of your earth and
you pro - vide the wine we of - fer, fruit of your earth and
look with fa - vour on our off - 'rings, pour out your Spi - rit

work of our hands.
work of our hands. Blest be the Lord for e - ver, A - men,
o - ver these gifts.

3rd time D.C. al Fine

blest be the Lord for e - ver, A - men.

3rd time D.C. al Fine

COME, HOLY GHOST

Text: John Cosin (1594-1672)
Music: Thomas Attwood (1765-1838) arr. Colin Hand

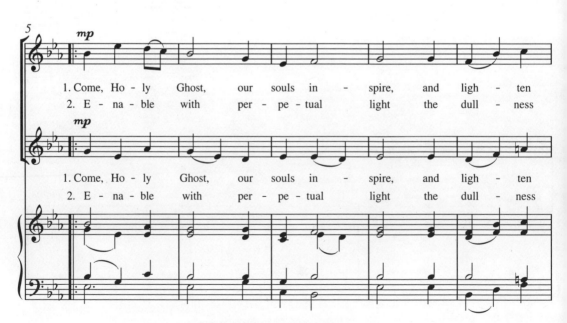

1. Come, Ho - ly Ghost, our souls in - spire, and ligh - ten
2. E - na - ble with per - pe - tual light the dull - ness

ter - nal me - rit, Fa - ther, Son, and Ho - ly

ter - nal me - rit, Fa - ther, Son, and Ho - ly

Spi - rit, Fa - ther, Son, and Ho - ly Spi - rit.

Spi - rit, Fa - ther, Son, and Ho - ly Spi - rit.

rit.

rit.

Anthems

COME, LET US ALL THIS DAY

Text: Revd John Troutbeck (1832-1899)
Music: Johann Sebastian Bach (1685-1750)

Ghost he - ro - ic hearts has fired, so let us pray that

ours by him may be in - spired.

Let him whom God in -

spires by ho - ly word and Spi - rit, to

whom is giv'n to share the Sa - viour's grace and me - rit, u - nite with us, and praise our God for e - ver true, whose mer - cies are this day, and ev - 'ry morn - ing new.

rall.

Anthems

COME ON AND CELEBRATE

Text and Music: Dave Bankhead and Patricia Morgan
arr. Christopher Tambling

101

ce - le - brate and sing, ce - le - brate and sing to the King.

to the King,

Come on and ce - le - brate, ce - le - brate,

sing to the King.

ce - le - brate and sing, ce - le - brate and sing to the King.

to the

King, sing to the King.

Come on and ce - le - brate

cresc.

ff

f

Ped.

Ah,

his gift of love, we will ce - le - brate the Son of God who loved us

we'll shout your praise, O King,

and gave us life.

you give us joy no-thing else can bring. Ah,

We'll give to you our

ce - le - bra - tion praise. Come on and

of - fer-ing in ce - le - bra - tion praise.

and sing to the King, sing to the King.

Ce - le - brate and sing to the King.

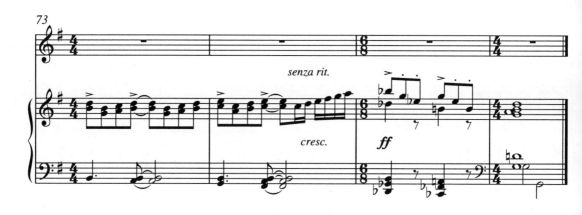

senza rit.

cresc.

ff

COME, PREPARE THE WAY

An Anthem for Advent

Text: Nick Fawcett (b.1957)
Music: Trumpet Voluntary (Jeremiah Clarke)
arr. Christopher Tambling

Come, pre - pare the way, make straight a path in the wil - der - ness; give

thanks and ce - le - brate, the pro - mised day is near.

Sopranos
mf (repeat ff)

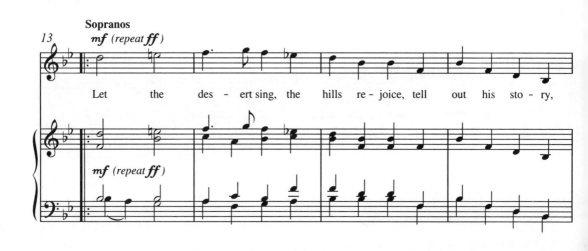

Let the des - ert sing, the hills re - joice, tell out his sto - ry,

let the hea - vens ring, the earth in greet - ing call.

Wel - come now the King, lift up your voice, pro - claim his glo - ry,

for he comes to bring new life, new hope to all.

Come, pre - pare the way, make straight a path in the wil - der - ness; give

thanks and ce-le-brate, the pro-mised day is near.

Sound out the trum-pets, sound out the trum-pets, he shall reign for e - ver-more.

Sing out his praise, sing out his prai - ses, wor-ship and a - dore.

Come, pre - pare the way, make straight a path in the wil - der - ness; give

thanks and ce - le - brate, the pro - mised day is near.

COME, SPIRIT OF OUR GOD

Text: Michael Forster (b.1946)
Music: Alan Rees (b.1946)

word we would o - bey. O teach us all we need to know of your most ho - ly

way.

Come with the gift of life, our

Man.

na - ture to re - fine; as sons and daugh-ters let us live,

and heirs of love di - vine.

Slightly slower

Give us a will-ing voice to speak in ev - 'ry

place, wher - e - ver doubts and fears con-fine, of li - be - ra - ting grace.

COME TO ME

Text: Matthew 11:28-30
Music: Margaret Rizza (b.1929)

115

and are hea-vy bur-dened, you shall find rest. Come to me,

you who la-bour and are hea-vy bur-dened, you shall find rest.

poco rit.

a tempo

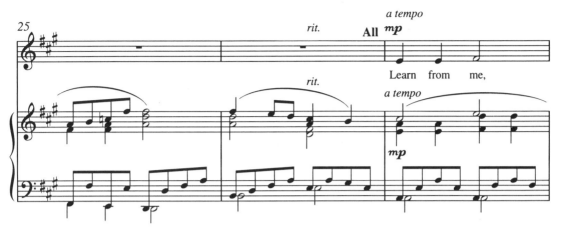

hum - ble of heart.

S: Come to me,

A: Come to me,

you who thirst; from my heart liv-ing wa-ters flow.

you who thirst; from my heart liv-ing wa-ters flow.

Measure 43: Come to me, you who thirst; from my heart

Measure 46: liv-ing wa-ters flow. Come to me, you who thirst;

poco rit. *a tempo*

Measure 49: from my heart liv-ing wa-ters flow. Come to me,

learn from me, come to me, learn from me.

You shall find rest, you shall find rest, you shall find rest.

DESIDERIUM ANIMAE

Text: Psalm 21:2-3
Music: George Malcolm (1917-1998)

Translation: You have granted him the desire of his heart
and have not withheld the request of his lips,
and placed a crown of pure gold on his head.
(NIV)

GIVE THANKS TO THE LORD OUR GOD

Text: Hubert J. Richards (b.1921), based on Psalms 103 (102) and 105 (104)
Music: Richard Lloyd (b.1933)

in his praise. Al - le - lu - ia, al - le -

Choir and Congregation

lu - ia, al - le - lu - ia. Al - le -

lu - ia, al - le - lu - ia, al - le -

lu - ia.

Choir *mf*

1. Praise God, who for-gives all our
3. As hea - ven is high a - bove

Man.

Choir and Congregation

sins   and   heals us   of ev – 'ry-thing e – vil;   he
earth,   so strong is   his love   for his   peo – ple.   As

res – cues our life from the grave   and clothes us in mer – cy and
far   as the east from the west,   so   far   he re-moves all our

love.   Al –   le – lu – ia,   al – le –
sins.

lu – ia,   al –   le – lu – ia.

Ped.

Man.

Choir *mp*

2. Our God is all kind-ness and love, so
4. As fa - thers take pi - ty on sons, we

pa - tient and rich in com - pas - sion; not treat - ing us as we de -
know God will show us com - pas - sion; while know-ing of what we are

serve; not pay - ing us back for our sins.
made; no more than the dust of the earth.

Choir and Congregation *f*

Al - le - lu - ia, al - le - lu - ia,

f

Ped.

125

al - le - lu - ia. Give thanks to the Lord our God.

Re - mem-ber all his bles - sings. Tell the whole world what he's done.

Choir and Congregation

Sing to him, sing in his praise. Al - le - lu - ia,

al - le - lu - ia, al - le - lu - ia.

GLADNESS, SADNESS, JOY AND SORROW

Introit
Text: Nick Fawcett (b.1957)
Music: To a Wild Rose (Edward MacDowell)
arr. Noel Rawsthorne

or to - mor - row, dreams and trou - bles, hopes and fears;

or to - mor - row, dreams and trou - bles, hopes and fears;

bring to Je - sus life in all its tur - moil,

bring all you face each

day, he will lead the way.

Come now, see how, Christ is wait - ing, reach - ing out to guide and bless; no more fight - ing, he - si - ta - ting, come to Je - sus, be at rest.

Man.

Ped.

129

GOD IS GOOD

Text and Music: Graham Kendrick (b.1950)
arr. Christopher Tambling

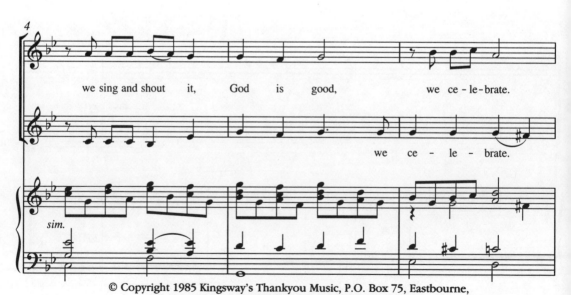

God is good, no more we doubt it, God is good, we we know it's true. And when I think of his love for me my heart know it's true. Man. fills with praise and I feel like danc - ing. For in his heart there is

room for me and I run with arms o-pen wide.

Sopranos and Altos

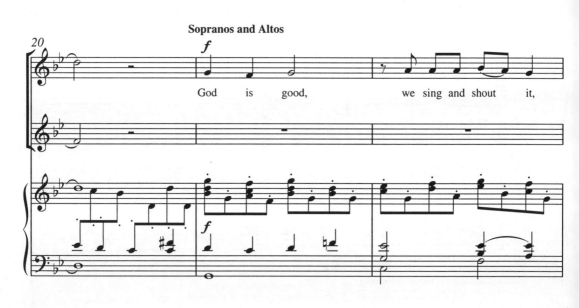

God is good, we sing and shout it,

God is good, we ce - le - brate. God is good,

no more we doubt it, God is good, we know it's

true.   We know it's true.

GOD SO LOVED THE WORLD

Text: John 3:16
Music: John Stainer (1840-1901) arr. Colin Hand

Anthems

GOD WHO MADE THE EARTH

Text: Sarah Betts Rhodes (c.1870)
Music: Malcolm Archer (b.1952)

GREAT INDEED ARE YOUR WORKS, O LORD

Text and Music: Aniceto Nazareth

1. The u - ni - verse, night and day,   tells of all your
2. You are the path which we tread,   you will lead us
3. You lead them all by the hand   to the heav'n - ly

1. The u - ni - verse, night and day,   tells of all your
2. You are the path which we tread,   you will lead us
3. You lead them all by the hand   to the heav'n - ly

won - ders.   You are our life and our light:
on - ward.   From ev - 'ry cor - ner of earth
king - dom.   Then, at the end of all times,

won - ders.   You are our life and our light:
on - ward.   From ev - 'ry cor - ner of earth
king - dom.   Then, at the end of all times,

we shall praise you al - ways.
all the na - tions ga - ther.
you will come in glo - ry.

we shall praise you al - ways.
all the na - tions ga - ther.
you will come in glo - ry.

D.C.

145

HÆC DIES

Text: The Liturgy of Easter
Music: Colin Mawby (b.1936)

Translation: This day was made by the Lord; let us be glad and rejoice in it.
Praise the Lord, for he is good: since his mercy lasts for ever.

ex - sul - te - mus, et læ - te - mur in

ex - sul - te - mus, et læ - te - mur in

e - a.   Con - fi - te - mi - ni   Do - mi - no,   quo -

e - a.   Con - fi - te - mi - ni   Do - mi - no,   quo -

- ni - am   bo - nus: quo - ni - am   in

- ni - am   bo - nus:

HALLELUJAH CHORUS

Text: from Scripture
Music: George Frideric Handel (1685-1759) arr. Colin Hand

153

King of kings,

e -ver, hal -le -lu -jah, hal -le - lu -jah, for e -ver and

e -ver, hal -le -lu -jah, hal -le - lu -jah, for e -ver and

(+ Reed)

Ped.

and Lord of lords,

e -ver, hal -le -lu -jah, hal -le - lu -jah, for e -ver and

e -ver, hal -lc- lu -jah, hal -le - lu -jah, for e -ver and

HE SHALL FEED HIS FLOCK

Text: from Scripture
Music: George Frideric Handel (1685-1759) arr. Colin Hand

shep - herd, and he shall ga - ther the lambs with his arm,

with his arm, and car - ry them

in his bo - som, and gen - tly lead those that are with young, and

gen - tly lead those, and gen - tly lead those that are with young.

162

he will give you rest.   Take his yoke up-on you, and

learn of him, for he is meek and low-ly of heart, and

ye shall find rest, and ye shall find rest un-to your souls.

Take his yoke up-on you, and learn of him, for

he is meek and low - ly of heart, and ye shall find rest, and

ye shall find rest un - to your souls.

For Judy Long

HOLY GOD

Text: based on the Aaronic Blessing (Numbers 6:24-26)
Music: Kevin Mayhew (b.1942)

Ho - ly God, we place our - selves in - to your hands. Bless us

and care for us, be gra - cious and lov - ing to us;

look kind - ly up - on us, and give us peace.

HOLY SPIRIT, TRUTH DIVINE

Text: Samuel Longfellow (1819-1892)
Music: Alan Viner (b.1951)

Ho - ly Spi - rit, truth di-vine, dawn up-on this soul of mine;

word of God, and in - ward light, wake my spi - rit, clear my sight.

Accompaniment preferably for piano

Ho - ly Spi - rit, love di - vine, glow with - in this

heart of mine, kin - dle ev - 'ry high de - sire,

pe - rish self in thy pure fire.

*The lower notes may be played an octave higher if desired

HYMN TO THE HOLY SPIRIT

Text: Timothy Dudley-Smith (b.1926)
Music: Malcolm Archer (b.1952)

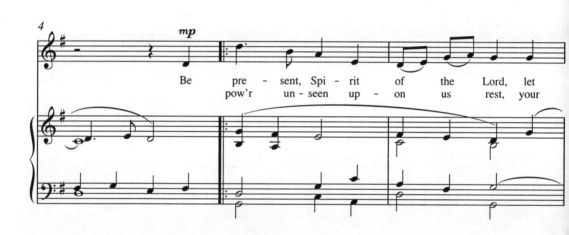

Be pre - sent, Spi - rit of the Lord, let
pow'r un - seen up - on us rest, your

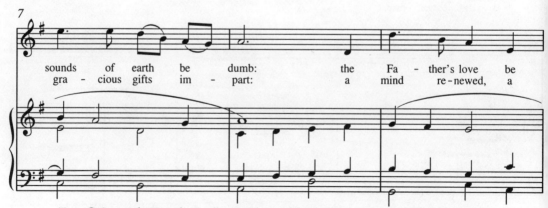

sounds of earth be dumb: the Fa - ther's love be
gra - cious gifts im - part: a mind re - newed, a

shed a - broad, the dew of bles - sing on us poured, O
spi - rit bless'd, a life where Christ is ma - ni - fest, an

si - lent Spi - rit, come!
un - der - stan - ding heart.

1.

In

2.

Love's sov - 'reign work of grace ful - fil, our

souls to Christ in - cline, in - tent to do the

Fa - ther's will and stand by faith be - fore him still in right - eous - ness di - vine, in right - eous - ness di - vine. O Spi - rit come, and with us stay; make

+ Gt. to Ped.

ev - 'ry heart your home. So work in us that

we who pray may walk with Christ in wis - dom's way – O

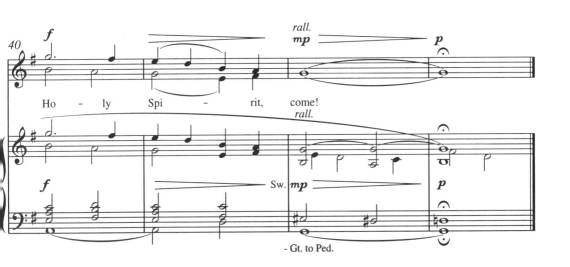

Ho - ly Spi - rit, come!

- Gt. to Ped.

I CALL ON THEE, LORD JESUS CHRIST

Text: Miles Coverdale (1487-1568)
Music: Stanley Vann (b.1910)

hold by thy word e - ver - more,

a - bove all thing, ne - ver re-

sist - ing but to in - crease in faith more and

rall.

rall.

more.

Tempo I

mp

IF ANYONE LOVES ME

Text: John 14:23
Music: Andrew Moore (b.1954)

11 they will keep my word,
they will keep my word, and my fa - ther will
Man.

14 will love them and we shall come to them.
love them, and we shall come to them.

Unison
17 *mp* *mf*
If a - ny - one loves me, if a - ny - one loves me
mp *mf*
Ped.

179

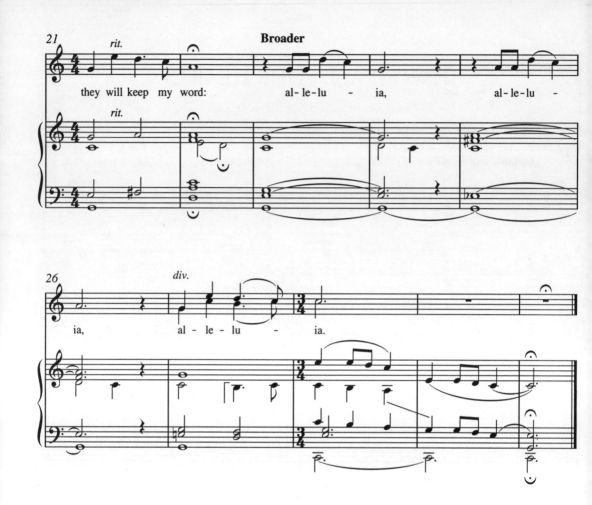

they will keep my word: al- le- lu - ia,   al- le- lu -

ia,   al - le - lu - ia.

IF WITH ALL YOUR HEARTS

Text: Deuteronomy 4:29; Job 23:3
Music: Felix Mendelssohn (1809-1847) arr. Harrison Oxley

find me; thus saith our God, thus saith our God.

O that I knew where I might find him, that I might ev-en come be-fore his pre - sence. O that I knew where I might find him, that I might ev-en come be-fore his pre - sence, come be-fore his pre - sence,

Man.

Ped.

Lyrics in the vocal line:

32 — O that I knew where I might find him.

37 — If with all your hearts ye tru-ly seek me ye shall ev-er sure-ly

42 — find me; thus saith our God, ye shall ev-er sure-ly find me;

47 — thus saith our God.

I WILL BE WITH YOU

Text (based on Matthew 28:19-20) and Music: Gerard Markland
arr. Christopher Tambling

Fine

Go now and spread my word!

Fine

1. Come, walk with me on stor -
2. And you, my friend, will you
3. Your life will be trans - formed
4. And if you say: 'Yes, Lord,

- my wa - ters. Why fear? Reach
now leave me, or do you
with pow - er by liv - ing
I love you,' then feed my

out, and I'll be there.
know me as your Lord?
tru - ly in my name.
lambs and feed my sheep.

D.C.

D.C.

185

Anthems

I WILL LIFT UP MINE EYES

Text: Psalm 121
Music: Noel Rawsthorne (b.1929)

day nei-ther the moon by night. The

Lord shall pre-serve thee from all e - vil, yea, it is e -ven he that shall keep thy

soul. The Lord shall pre-serve thy go-ing out and thy com - ing

in: from this time forth for e - ver - more.

I WILL MAGNIFY THEE, O LORD

Text: Psalm 30:1
Music: Joseph Corfe (1740-1820)

I will mag – ni – fy thee,

O Lord, O

O Lord, O

Lord, O Lord: for thou hast

Lord, O Lord: for thou, for thou hast

set   me   up,   and   made   me   to   tri   -

set   me   up,   and   made   me   to

rall.   *a tempo*

- umph   in   thy   sal - va - tion.

rall.   *a tempo*

tri - umph   in   thy   sal - va - tion.

rall.   *a tempo*

rall.

JESU, JOY OF OUR DESIRING

Text: Robert Bridges (1844-1930) alt.
Music: Johann Sebastian Bach (1685-1750) arr. Colin Hand

1. Je - su, joy of our de -
2. Through the way, where hope is

si - ring,   ho - ly wis - dom,
gui - ding,   hark, what peace - ful

si - ring,   ho - ly wis - dom,
gui - ding,   hark, what peace - ful

love most bright,
mu - sic rings,

love most bright,
mu - sic rings,

Word of God, our flesh that fa - shion'd,
Theirs is beau - ty's fair - est plea - sure,

Word of God, our flesh that fa - shion'd,
Theirs is beau - ty's fair - est plea - sure,

with the fire of
theirs is wis - dom's

with the fire of
theirs is wis - dom's

200

throne.
known.

throne.
known.

2nd time rall.

JESUS, YOU ARE THE WAY

Text: Pamela Hayes
Music: Margaret Rizza (b.1929)

head has found its rest in the beat - ing in your breast.

Je - sus, this a - lone can be my prayer, your pierced heart o - pen there.

Soprano Solo *mp*

Je - sus, you are the way that I can hear the word that's

Je - su, Je - su,

Je - su, Je - su,

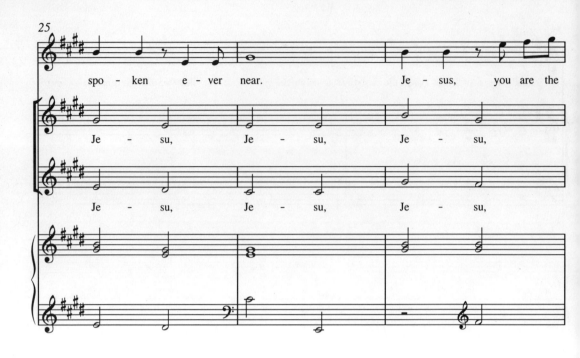

spo - ken e - ver near. Je - sus, you are the

Je - su, Je - su, Je - su,

Je - su, Je - su, Je - su,

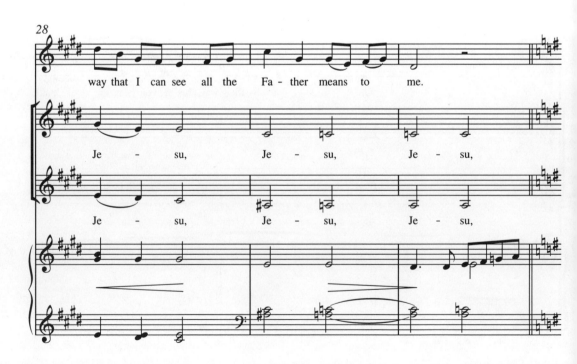

way that I can see all the Fa - ther means to me.

Je - su, Je - su, Je - su,

Je - su, Je - su, Je - su,

JESUS, YOU DIED FOR ME

Text: Nick Fawcett (b.1957)
Music: Adagio from Clarinet Concerto (Wolfgang Amadeus Mozart)
arr. Christopher Tambling

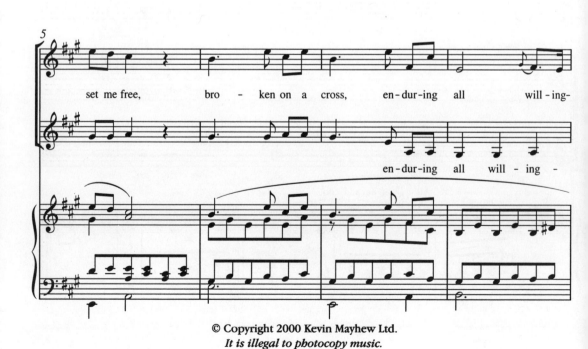

ly.   Je - sus,   what can I say?   How   can I such

ly.

love re-pay?   Though   my faith is poor,   I long to serve   you each

I long to serve you each

cresc.

day.   Lord,   I give to you.

cresc.

day.   All   I am and do,

cresc.

Reach out with your lov-ing hand and by your grace make me new.

mould me in your way,

Hold me fast, I pray,

teach me what it means to serve, for true to you I would stay.

LAUDATE DOMINUM

Text: Psalm 150
Music: Giuseppe Ottavio Pitoni (1657-1743) arr. Colin Hand

da - te e - um in fir - ma - men - to vir - tu - tis

da - te e - um in fir - ma - men - to vir - tu - tis

e - jus. Lau - da - te e - um in vir - tu - ti-bus e -

e - jus. Lau - da - te e - um in vir - tu - ti-bus e -

jus; lau - da - te e - um se - cun - dum mul - ti - tu - di-

jus; lau - da - te e - um se - cun - dum mul - ti - tu - di-

te – ri – o et ci – tha – ra, lau – da – te e – um in

te – ri – o et ci – tha – ra, lau – da – te e – um in

cym – ba – lis be – ne so – nan – ti – bus: om – nis spi – ri – tus

cym – ba – lis be – ne so – nan – ti – bus: om – nis spi – ri – tus

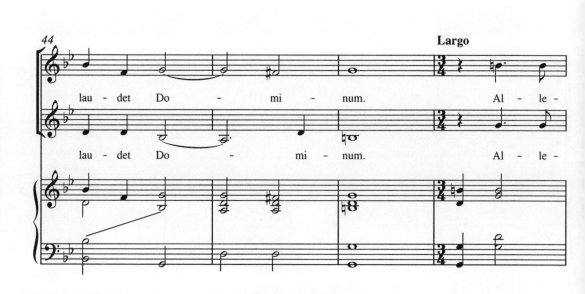

Largo

lau – det Do – mi – num. Al – le –

lau – det Do – mi – num. Al – le –

lu - ia, al - le - lu - ia, al - le - lu - ia, al - le -

lu - ia, al - le - lu - ia, al - le - lu - ia, al - le -

lu - ia, al - le - lu - ia, al - le - lu - ia.

lu - ia, al - le - lu - ia, al - le - lu - ia.

LAUDATE DOMINUM

Text: Psalm 117

Music: Wolfgang Amadeus Mozart (1756-1791) arr. Colin Hand

SA parts are optional: hum quietly

in ae - ter - num.

p
Glo -

- ri - a pa - tri et fi - li - o

et spi - ri - tu-i san - cto, si -

et spi - ri - tu-i san - cto, si -

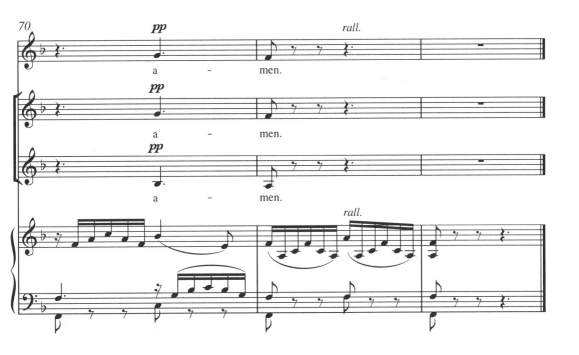

LEAD, KINDLY LIGHT

Text: John Henry Newman (1801-1890)
Music: Malcolm Archer (b.1952)

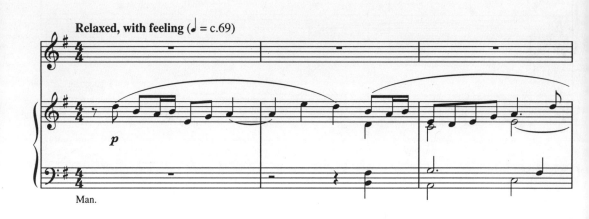

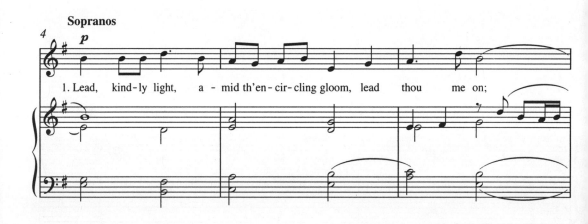

thou me on. Keep thou my feet; I do not ask to see the dis - tant scene; one step e - nough for me.

2. I was not e - ver thus, nor prayed that thou shouldst lead me on;

I loved to choose and see my path; but

now lead me on. I loved the gar - ish

day, and spite of fears, pride ruled my will: re - mem - ber not past

years.   3. So long thy pow'r hath blest me,   sure it

mf

still will lead me on, o'er moor and fen, o'er crag and for-est till the night is gone; and with the morn those an-gel fa-ces smile, which I have loved long since, and lost a - while.

Lead thou me on,

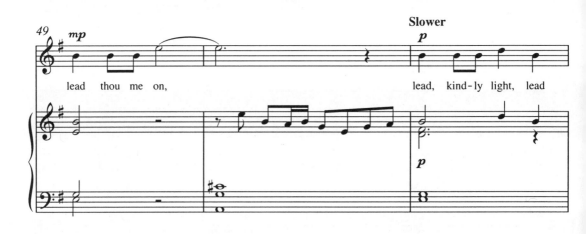

lead thou me on,   lead, kind-ly light, lead

Slower

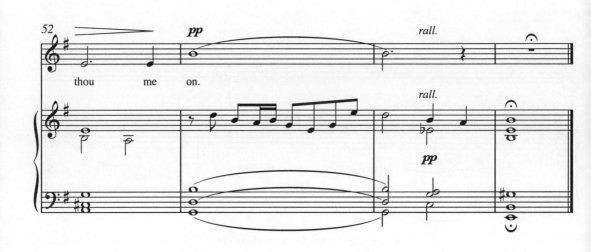

thou   me   on.

rall.

LEAD ME, LORD

Text: Psalm 5:8; 4:9
Music: Samuel Sebastian Wesley (1810-1876) arr. Colin Hand

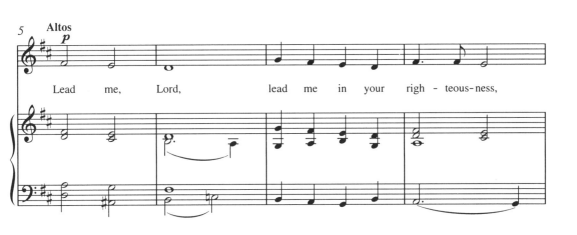

Lead me, Lord, lead me in your righ - teous-ness,

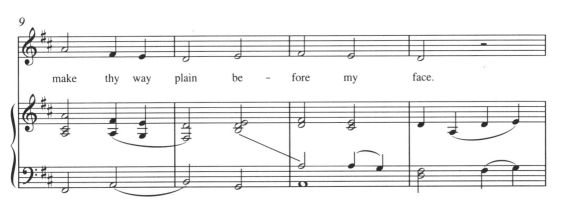

make thy way plain be - fore my face.

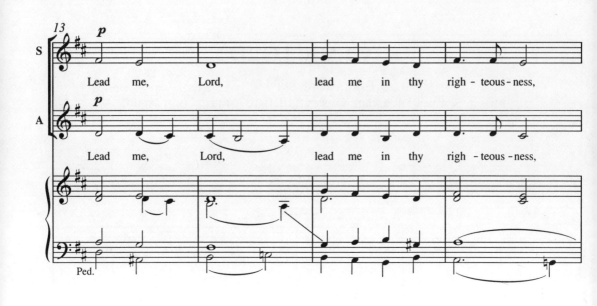

Lead me, Lord, lead me in thy righ-teous-ness,

Lead me, Lord, lead me in thy righ-teous-ness,

Ped.

make thy way plain be — fore my face.

make thy way plain be — fore my face.

Man.

Sopranos

For it is thou, Lord, thou, Lord, on-ly, that

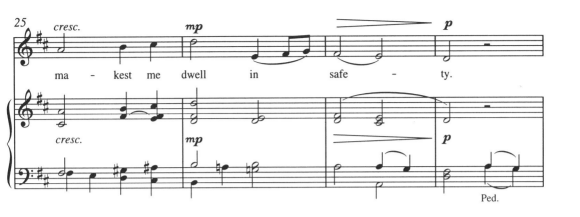

ma - kest me dwell in safe - ty.

For it is thou, Lord, thou, Lord, on - ly, that

For it is thou, Lord, thou, Lord, on - ly, that

ma - kest me dwell in safe - ty.

ma - kest me dwell in safe - ty.

For Russell Burton and the Hurstpierpoint College 10th annual preparatory schools festival

LET ALL THE WORLD IN EVERY CORNER SING

Text: George Herbert (1593-1633)
Music: Malcolm Archer (b.1952)

church with psalms must shout,   no door can keep them out.   But

church with psalms must shout,   no door can keep them out.   But

a - bove all the heart   must bear   the long - est

a - bove all the heart   must bear   the long - est

part.   Let all the world   in ev - 'ry

part.   Let all the world

Ped.

LET LOVE BE REAL

Text: Michael Forster (b.1946)
Music: Christopher Tambling (b.1964)

ten - ding,   where ev - 'ry weak - ness may be safe - ly known.   Give me your
liv - ing,   and makes us brave   to be what we might be.   Give me your
plete - ness,   and share the joy   of learn - ing to be whole.   Give me your

ten - ding,   where ev - 'ry weak - ness may be safe - ly known.   Give me your
liv - ing,   and makes us brave   to be what we might be.   Give me your
plete - ness,   and share the joy   of learn - ing to be whole.   Give me your

hand,   a - long the des - ert path - way,   give me your love   wher - e - ver we may
strength when   all my words are weak - ness,   give me your love   in spite of all you
hope, through dreams and dis - ap - point - ments,   give me your trust   when all my fail - ings

hand,   a - long the des - ert path - way, give me your love   wher - e - ver we may
strength when   all my words are weak - ness, give me your love   in spite of all you
hope, through dreams and dis - ap - point - ments, give me your trust   when all my fail - ings

go.
know.
show.
Still be my friend, my cri-tic and my lo - ver; don't make me

go.
know.
show.
Still be my friend, my cri-tic and my lo - ver; don't make me

change, don't make me strange, but let me grow.

To verses 2 and 3

2. Let love be   grow.
3. Let love be

Last time

change, don't make me strange, but let me grow.

2. Let love be   grow.
3. Let love be

Ped.

239

LET OUR PRAISE TO YOU

Text: Bryan Spinks, based on Psalm 141
Music: Malcolm Archer (b.1952)

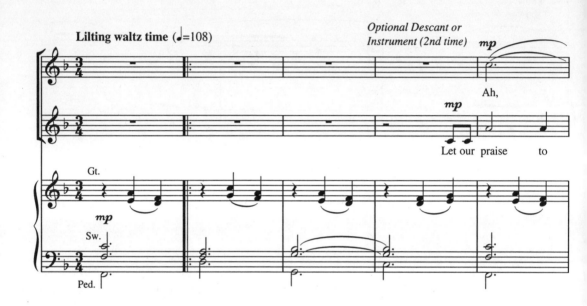

LIFT UP YOUR HEADS, O YE GATES

Text: from Scripture
Music: George Frideric Handel (1685-1759) arr. Colin Hand

249

ry, the King of Glo - ry, he

ry, the King of Glo - ry, he

Man.

is the King of Glo-ry, he is the King of Glo-ry, of Glo - ry.

is the King of Glo-ry, he is the King of Glo-ry, of Glo - ry.

Ped.

LISTEN

Text and Music: Aniceto Nazareth
arr. Malcolm Archer

Lis - ten, let your heart keep seek - ing; lis - ten to his con - stant speak - ing;

sempre staccato

lis - ten to the Spi - rit call - ing you.

Lis - ten to his in - spi - ra - tion; lis - ten to his in - vi - ta - tion;

17
Last time to Coda
lis - ten to the Spi - rit call - ing you.
21
mf cresc.
1. He's in the sound of the thun - der, in the whis - per of the breeze.
2. He's in the laugh - ter of child - ren, in the pat - ter of the rain.
3. He's in the noise of the ci - ty, in the sing - ing of the birds.
legato
mf cresc.
Ped.
25
mf cresc.
dim.
D.S.
He's in the might of the whirl - wind, in the roar - ing of the seas.
Hear him in cries of the suff - 'ring, in their moan - ing and their pain.
And in the night - time, the still - ness helps you lis - ten to his word.
D.S.
mf cresc.
dim.
CODA
Soprano Solo
29
pp
rall.
Lis - ten to the Spi - rit call - ing you.
rall.
pp
Ped.

Anthems

LORD, I LIFT MY HANDS TO YOU

Text: Nick Fawcett (b.1957)
Music: Adagio from Pathétique Sonata (Ludwig van Beethoven)
arr. Noel Rawsthorne

tur - moil, heart crushed by care.

tur - moil, heart crushed by care.

Gt.

Soprano Solo

Come to me and find rest for your soul. Don't

Gt.

Sw.

wor - ry, simp-ly trust me, my love can make you

LORD, YOU HAVE TOUCHED MY LIFE

Text: Nick Fawcett (b.1957)
Music: Slow movement from 'Emperor' Concerto (Ludwig van Beethoven)
arr. Christopher Tambling

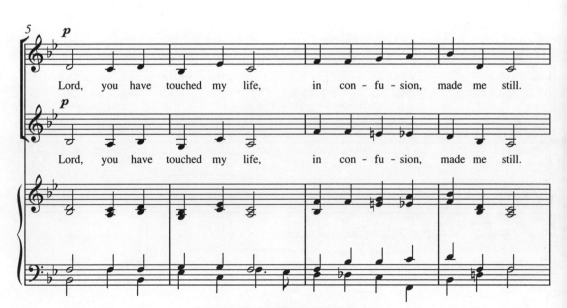

Lord, you have touched my life, in con-fu-sion, made me still.

Lord, you have touched my life, in con-fu-sion, made me still.

Storms have ceased, my mind at peace. No more tears,

Storms have ceased, my mind at peace. No more tears,

no more fears; qui - et - ness in - stead of strife:

no more fears; qui - et - ness in - stead of strife:

qui - et - ness in - stead of strife.

qui - et - ness in - stead of strife.

Lord, you have touched my soul, in my weak - ness

Though each day I go a - stray,

shown me grace.

you are there, in your care, reach - ing out to

you are there, in your care, reach - ing out to

hope re - born, like the dawn, life is just a -
hope re - born, like the dawn, life is just a -

bout to start! Life is just a - bout to
bout to start! Life is just a - bout to

start! You have touched, you have touched my life.
start! You have touched, you have touched my life.

LOVE THE LORD

Text: Luke 10:27
Music: Andrew Moore (b.1954)

self, you must love with all your strength, and your

self, you must love with all your strength, and your

neigh - bour as your - self.

neigh - bour as your - self.

You must love the Lord your

For Jessie, with love

MAGNIFICAT

Text: Michael Forster (b.1946)
Music: Kevin Mayhew (b.1942)

Quasi calypso

1. Join the song of praise and pro - test, all the na-tions of the earth:

God, who loves the poor and hum - ble, sings of dig-ni- ty and worth.

Those the world has long re - ject - ed take at last their right - ful place,

2. God has rocked the earth's foundations,
   turned its values upside-down:
   strength is overcome by weakness
   and the humble wear the crown.
   Now the pow'r of God in action
   undermines the nations' pride,
   lifts the poor and feeds the hungry,
   pushing rich and proud aside.

3. Join the song of praise and protest
   as the voiceless find a voice,
   as the pow'rless rise triumphant
   and the broken hearts rejoice.
   Now the God of all creation
   rights the long-accepted wrongs;
   let the voices of the nations
   swell the liberation song.

MAY THE LORD BLESS YOU

Text: Gaelic Blessing, adapted by Margaret Rizza (b.1929)
Music: Margaret Rizza

ah,

his light shine up - on you, his peace sur - round you, his love en - fold you.

his light shine up - on you, his peace sur - round you, his love en - fold you.

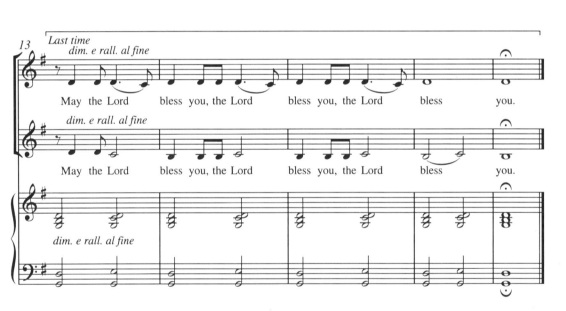

Last time
dim. e rall. al fine

May the Lord bless you, the Lord bless you, the Lord bless you.

dim. e rall. al fine

May the Lord bless you, the Lord bless you, the Lord bless you.

dim. e rall. al fine

MORNING HAS BROKEN

Text: Eleanor Farjeon (1881-1965)
Music: Traditional Gaelic melody arr. Christopher Tambling

pass. Ah,

Mine is the sun - light! Mine is the morn - ing born of the

one light E - den saw play! Praise with e - la - tion, praise ev - 'ry

morn - ing, God's re - cre - a - tion of the new day!

ah,

ah,

ah.

Descant

All, unison

Ped.

For the St Edmund's Young People's Choir

O ETERNAL GOD

Text: Jeremy Taylor (1613-1667)
Music: Kevin Mayhew (b.1942)

O e-ter-nal God, help-er of the help-less, com-for-ter of the com-fort-less, hope of the af-flict-ed, bread of the hun-gry, drink of the thirs-ty and sa-viour of all who wait up-on you:

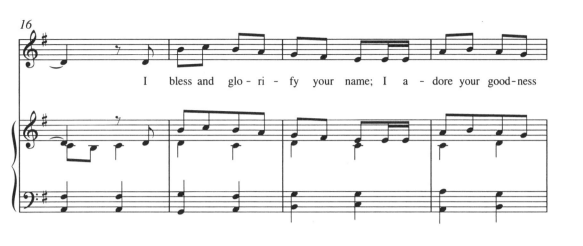

I bless and glo - ri - fy your name; I a - dore your good - ness

and de - light in your love. Take from me ev - 'ry

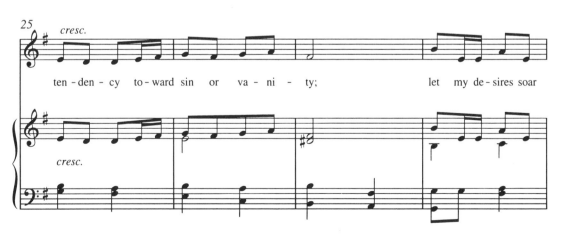

cresc.

ten - den - cy to - ward sin or va - ni - ty; let my de - sires soar

cresc.

up - wards to your love, that I may hun - ger and

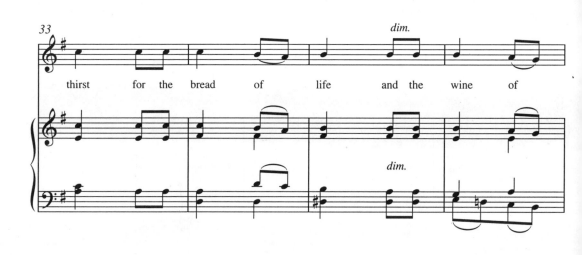

thirst for the bread of life and the wine of

heav'n, and know no love but yours.

Anthems

O FOR THE WINGS OF A DOVE

Text: Psalm 55:6-7
Music: Felix Mendelssohn (1809-1847) arr. Colin Hand

O LORD, MY HEART IS NOT PROUD

Text: Psalm 131
Music: Margaret Rizza (b.1929)

* *Sing either part*

O LOVE, I GIVE MYSELF TO THEE

Text: J. Scheffler trans. Catherine Winkworth (1827-1878)
Music: William Lloyd Webber (1914-1982)

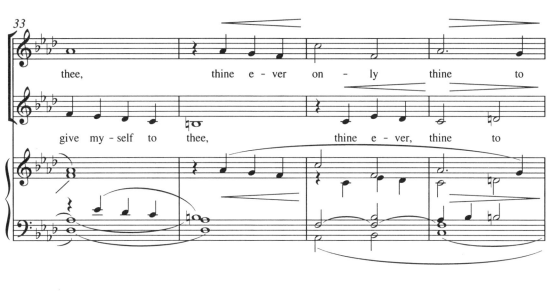

thee, thine e - ver on - ly thine to

give my - self to thee, thine e - ver, thine to

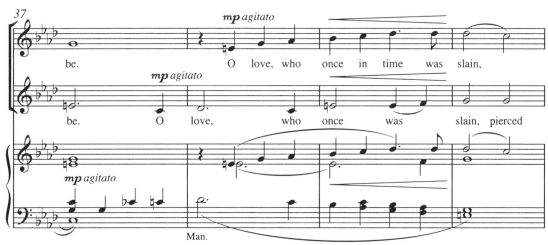

be. O love, who once in time was slain,

be. O love, who once was slain, pierced

Man.

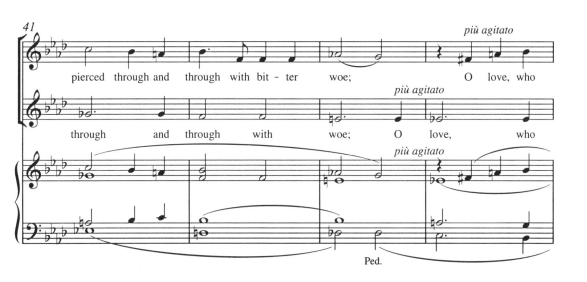

pierced through and through with bit - ter woe; O love, who

through and through with woe; O love, who

Ped.

O love, who once shalt bid me rise from out this
O love, who once shalt bid me rise from out

dy - ing life of ours; O love, who once o'er yon - der skies shalt
this dy - ing life of ours; who once shalt

set me in the fade - less bow'rs: O love, I give my - self to
set me in the fade - less bow'rs: O love, O love, I

Anthems

O SING UNTO THE LORD

Text: Psalm 149
Music: Noel Rawsthorne (b.1929)

PANIS ANGELICUS

Text: Thomas Aquinas (1227-1274)
Music: César Franck (1822-1890) arr. Alan Ridout and John Ballantine

Translation: The bread of angels becomes bread for humans; the bread of heaven is the fulfilment of its foreshadowing. What a wonder! The Lord becomes the food of his poor and lowly servant.

Anthems

PEACE, PERFECT PEACE

Text: Kevin Mayhew (b.1942)
Music: Kevin Mayhew arr. Christopher Tambling

Thus, says the Lord, will the world know my friends.
Thus, says the Lord, will the world know my friends.

Peace, per - fect peace, is the gift of Christ our Lord.
Faith, per - fect faith, is the gift of Christ our Lord.

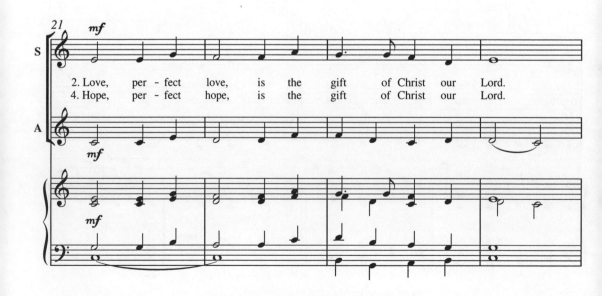

2. Love, per - fect love, is the gift of Christ our Lord.
4. Hope, per - fect hope, is the gift of Christ our Lord.

Love, per - fect love, is the gift of Christ our Lord.
Love, per - fect love, is the gift of Christ our Lord.

Thus, says the Lord, will the world know my friends.
Thus, says the Lord, will the world know my friends.

1.

Love, per - fect love, is the gift of Christ our Lord.
Hope, per - fect hope, is the gift of Christ our

1.

mp

world know my friends. Joy, per-fect joy, is the

gift of Christ our Lord.

PIE JESU

Text: from the Requiem Mass
Music: Gabriel Fauré (1845-1924) arr. Alan Ridout

Translation: Holy Lord Jesus, give them everlasting rest.

PRAISE OUR GOD

Text: Hubert J. Richards (b.1921)
Music: Andrew Moore (b.1954)

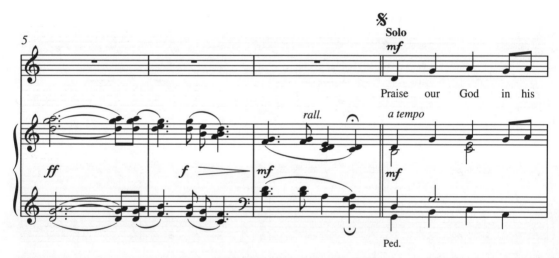

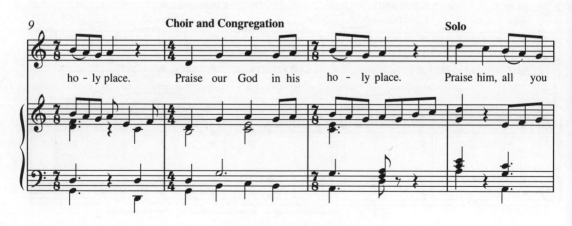

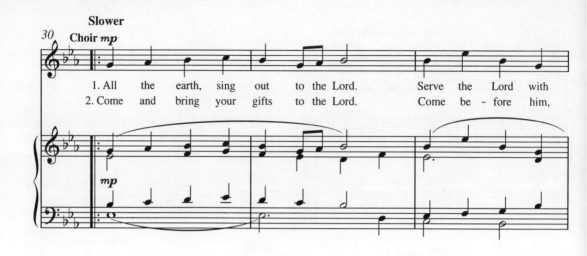

Slower

Choir *mp*

1. All the earth, sing out to the Lord. Serve the Lord with
2. Come and bring your gifts to the Lord. Come be - fore him,

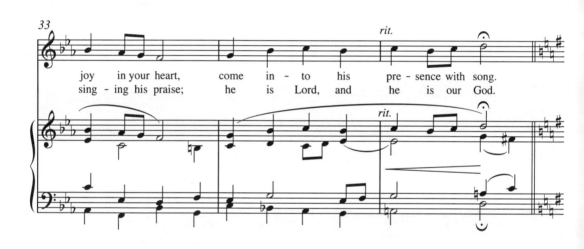

rit.

joy in your heart, come in - to his pre - sence with song.
sing - ing his praise; he is Lord, and he is our God.

Tempo I

Solo   **Choir and Congregation**

Al - le - lu - ia, al - le - lu - ia.   Al - le - lu - ia, al - le - lu - ia.

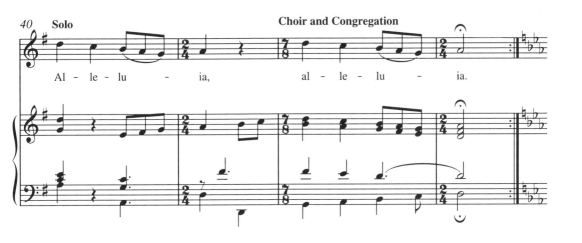

Solo ... Choir and Congregation

Al - le - lu - ia, al - le - lu - ia.

Slower
Choir *mp*

3. God is good, his love ne - ver ends; he is al - ways

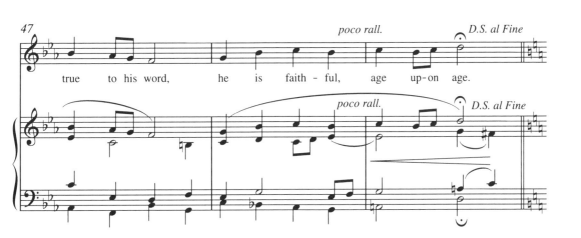

true to his word, he is faith - ful, age up-on age.

poco rall. *D.S. al Fine*

PRAISE TO THE LORD

Text: Hubert J. Richards (b.1921) based on Psalm 95
Music: Richard Lloyd (b.1933)

all the earth, and ring out your prai - ses to God.
in his house, the Lord who made hea - ven and earth.

Bles - sed be God for

e - ver, A - men, bles - sed be God for e - ver, A - men, bles - sed be God for

2nd time to

e - ver, A - men.

Choir *mf*

2. Come, tell of his won-der-ful deeds;

come, thank him for what he has done, and of - fer your gifts to the Lord.

Praise to the Lord, the king of cre-a-tion, praise to the Lord, for he is our sal-va-tion. Come to his al-tar, come, ev-'ry na-tion, bow with his peo-ple in a-do-ra-tion. Bles-sed be God for e-ver, A-men, bles-sed be God for e-ver, A-men,

bles - sed be God   for   e - ver, A -   men.

Anthems

For Neil Shroff and the Auckland Boys' Choir, New Zealand.

PRAISE TO THE LORD, THE ALMIGHTY

Text: Joachim Neander (1640-1680), trans. Catherine Winkworth (1827-1878)
Music: Malcolm Archer (b.1952)

how thy heart's wi - shes hath been   grant-ed in what   he or -

how thy heart's wi - shes hath been   grant-ed in what   he or -

dain - eth?   grant-ed in what   he or - dain   -

dain - eth?   grant-ed in what   he or - dain   -

eth?

eth?

Man.   Ped.

321

3. Praise to the Lord, who doth pros- per thy work and de- fend thee;
sure- ly his good- ness and mer- cy shall dai- ly at-
tend thee: pon- der a- new
what the Al- migh- ty can do, if to the end

he be - friend thee.

poco a poco cresc.

4. Praise to the Lord, O let all that is in me a - dore

4. Praise to the Lord, O let all that is in me a -

PROCLAIM THE STORY

Text: Nick Fawcett (b.1957)
Music: Te Deum Prelude (Marc-Antoine Charpentier)
arr. Noel Rawsthorne

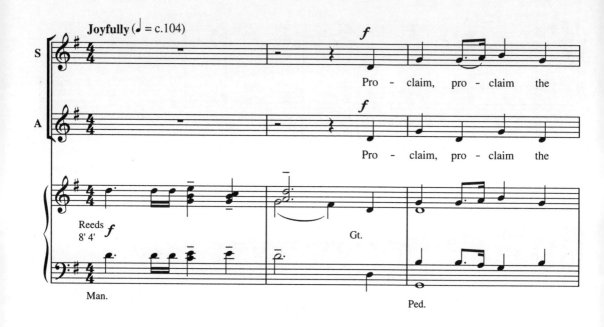

known to all his glo - ry, lift up his name on

known to all his glo - ry, lift up his name on

high!

high!

He comes to reign for e - ver - more, come

He comes to reign for e - ver - more, come

kneel, a - dore, bow down in awe; lift up your hearts and

kneel, a - dore, bow down in awe; lift up your hearts and

wor - ship Christ, whom God has crowned as Lord!

wor - ship Christ, whom God has crowned as Lord!

joice and greet the King of kings! Lift high his roy - al

joice and greet the King of kings! Lift high his roy - al

rall.

ban - ner, lift up your voice and sing.

ban - ner, lift up your voice and sing.

rall.

SAVE US, O LORD

Text: The Office of Compline
Music: Kevin Mayhew (b.1942)

SEND FORTH YOUR SPIRIT

Text: Psalm 104
Music: Margaret Rizza (b.1929)

16 To verses | Last time — Fine

re - new the face of the earth.

Fine

earth. earth, re - new the face of the earth.

earth. earth, re - new the face of the earth.

Fine

20 Unison

1. Bless the Lord, O my soul, O Lord God, how great you are; you are
2. Lord, how great are your works, in wis-dom you made them all; all the
3. May your wis-dom en-dure, re-joice in your works, O Lord. I will

24 D.S. al Fine

clothed in ho-nour and glo-ry, you set the world on its foun-da-tions.
earth is full of your crea-tures, your hand al-ways o-pen to feed them.
sing for e-ver and e-ver, in praise of my God and my King.

D.S. al Fine

SEND FORTH YOUR SPIRIT, O LORD

Text: Aniceto Nazareth, based on Psalm 104
Music: Aniceto Nazareth

Send forth your Spi-rit, O Lord, that the face of the earth be re - newed.

Ah, ah,

1. O my soul, a - rise and bless the Lord God. Say to

ah,

him: 'My God, how great you are. You are clothed with ma-jes-ty and

splen-dour, and light is the gar-ment you wear.'

D.C.

D.C.

2. 'You have built your palace on the waters.
Like the winds, the angels do your word.
You have set the earth on its foundation,
so firm, to be shaken no more.'

3. 'All your creatures look to you for comfort;
from your open hand they have their fill.
You send forth your Spirit and revive them,
the face of the earth you renew.'

4. While I live, I sing the Lord God's praises;
I will thank the author of these marvels.
Praise to God, the Father, Son and Spirit
both now and for ever. Amen.

SILENT, SURRENDERED

Text: v.1: Pamela Hayes; v.2: Margaret Rizza (b.1929)
Music: Margaret Rizza

Additional verse for use during Pentecost

SING ALOUD, THE DAY IS BREAKING

Text: Nick Fawcett (b.1957)
Music: Ode to Joy (Ludwig van Beethoven)
arr. Noel Rawsthorne

Birds are call-ing, songs en-thrall-ing, fill the air with psalms of praise, in

Birds are call-ing, songs en-thrall-ing, fill the air with psalms of praise, in

the ci-ty sud-den bus-tle, in the mea-dow cat-tle graze.

the ci-ty sud-den bus-tle, in the mea-dow cat-tle graze.

mf   *cresc.*   *f*

Dew-drops glis-ten, gent-ly chris-ten life re-newed and hope re-born; ce-

mf   *cresc.*   *f*

Dew-drops glis-ten, gent-ly chris-ten life re-newed and hope re-born; ce-

mf   *cresc.*   *f*

- le - brate with all cre - a - tion, greet the mi - ra - cle of dawn.

- le - brate with all cre - a - tion, greet the mi - ra - cle of dawn.

dim.

Sing a - loud, the night is end - ed, morn - ing bathes the world with joy,

Sing a - loud, the night is end - ed, morn - ing bathes the world with joy,

sin and death have been trans-cend-ed, no-thing now can hope des-troy.

sin and death have been trans-cend-ed, no-thing now can hope des-troy.

Shin-ing af - ter tears comes laugh-ter, bro-ken hearts be - gin to heal, grave -

Shin-ing af - ter tears comes laugh-ter, bro-ken hearts be - gin to heal, grave -

- clothes ly - ing neat-ly fold-ed, can what they pro-claim be real?

- clothes ly - ing neat-ly fold-ed, can what they pro-claim be real?

Mist is clear-ing, faith ap - pear-ing, con - quers fear and scat - ters gloom, ce -

- le - brate with all cre - a - tion: Christ is ris - en from the tomb!

Anthems

For Hannah, with love

SING, HOLY MOTHER

Text: Michael Forster (b.1946)
Music: Kevin Mayhew (b.1942)

1. Bles - sed are you a - mong wo - men, full of mys - te - ri - ous
2. Stand with the lost and the lone - ly, those whom the vain world de -
3. Sing of the va - lues of hea - ven, shame our re - spec - ta - ble

grace; hold - ing the hopes of cre - a - tion
nies, join with the weak and the fool - ish,
pride! Sing to the spurned and the fear - ful,

in your ma - ter - nal em - brace.
hum - bling the strong and the wise! Sing, Ho - ly
tell them no long - er to hide!

D.S.

D.S.

Composed for the M.M.A in memory of Stanley Milne

SING PRAISE AND THANKSGIVING

Text: Paul Gerhardt (1607-1676) trans. M. Barclay (b.1951),
adapted by Colin Gibson and Malcolm Archer (b.1952)
Music: Malcolm Archer

33

ma - king he brings to their wa - king; in dark - ness he

37

held us in his gra - cious care, now in - to the

41

mf

light we are called from our sleep - ing. O praise our cre -

mf

45

a - tor, O praise our cre -

Sing his praise, O praise our cre - a - tor, sing

O praise our cre - a - tor, sing

praise to our

praise to our

God!

God!

SING TO THE LORD

Text: Nick Fawcett (b.1957)
Music: Marche Militaire (Franz Schubert)
arr. Christopher Tambling

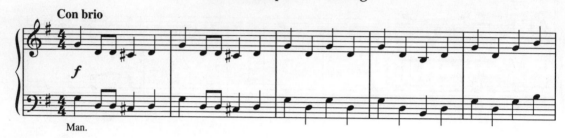

Sing to the Lord, sing a - loud of his ma - je - sty,

lift up your hearts, at his feet your prai - ses bring.

Tell of his love and faith-ful-ness, gra-cious-ness, ho - li -ness, let all the world his great name bless, wor - ship now the King! Sing to the Lord, sing a - loud of his glo - ry, lift up your souls, let our

sov-'reign God be a - dored.
Tell of his pow'r and right-eous-ness, gen-tle-ness,

stead-fast-ness, let ev-'ry-one his name con-fess, wor-ship now the Lord!

Man.

To the Lord sing praise!

Ped.

SOFTLY, TREAD SOFTLY

Text: Michael Forster (b.1946)
Music: Kevin Mayhew (b.1942)

Soft - ly, tread soft - ly as we fol - low where Je - sus trod,

Soft - ly, tread soft - ly as we fol - low where Je - sus trod,

soft - ly, tread soft - ly for we fol - low in the foot - steps of God.

soft - ly, tread soft - ly for we fol - low God.

1. Let us fol-low Je-sus to the place where he has led, let us wor-ship him who was

wor-ship him who was

killed and bu-ried, who is ri-sen from the dead.

killed and bu-ried, who is ri-sen from the dead.

Refrain

Soft-ly, tread soft-ly as we fol-low where Je-sus trod,

Soft-ly, tread soft-ly as we fol-low where Je-sus trod,

softly, tread softly for we follow in the footsteps of God.

softly, tread softly for we follow God.

2. Let us follow Jesus as we walk upon this earth,

let us find him living in the

world he died for, and proclaim its priceless worth.

and proclaim its priceless worth.

357

3. Let us fol-low Je-sus and an-nounce his reign of peace till the sick are healed and the

3. Let us fol-low Je-sus and an-nounce his reign of peace till the sick are healed and the

poor get jus-tice, and the cap-tives find re - lease.

poor get jus-tice, and the cap-tives find re - lease, the cap-tives find re-lease.

Refrain
Unison *p*

Soft - ly, tread soft - ly as we fol-low where Je - sus trod,

soft - ly, tread soft - ly for we fol-low in the foot-steps of God.

4. Let us fol-low Je-sus, let us join him in his way, let us tell the world that the

let us tell the world that the

night is o - ver, and it's re - sur - rec - tion day!

night is o - ver, and it's re - sur - rec - tion day!

Refrain
Unison *p*

Soft - ly, tread soft - ly as we fol-low where Je - sus trod,

soft - ly, tread soft - ly for we fol-low in the foot-steps of God.

SONG FOR A YOUNG PROPHET

Text: Damian Lundy (1940-1997) based on Jeremiah 1
Music: Damian Lundy arr. Malcolm Archer

Last time

mind.

rall.

1. Be - fore I formed you in the womb I knew you through and through, I chose you to be mine. Be-fore you left your mo-ther's side I called to you, my child, to be my sign.

D.S.

2. I know that you are very young,
   but I will make you strong;
   I'll fill you with my word;
   and you will travel through the land,
   fulfilling my command
   which you have heard.

3. And ev'rywhere you are to go
   my hand will follow you;
   you will not be alone.
   In all the danger that you fear
   you'll find me very near,
   your word's my own.

4. With all my strength you will be filled;
   you will destroy and build,
   for that is my design.
   You will create and overthrow,
   reap harvests I will sow;
   your word is mine.

SOUND OUT HIS PRAISES!

Text: Nick Fawcett (b.1957)
Music: Hornpipe from the 'Water Music' (George Frideric Handel)
arr. Christopher Tambling

scents, the touch, the tastes, the sounds, so much! The joys each

scents, the tastes, the sounds, so much! The love which thrills our hearts,

day im-parts, he made them all. Re-joice, sing prai-ses to

him!

Man.

He brought our world to birth, great things he's done. Lift up your

voice and praise the Lord! He is our sov-'reign God, the migh-ty

one. Lift up your voice and praise the Lord!

TAKE MY HANDS, LORD

Text: vs. 1 and 3: Margaret Rizza (b.1929); v.2: Anon.
Music: Margaret Rizza

Performance suggestion: v.1 all voices in unison on Soprano part
v.2 harmony
v.3 harmony with descant

lone - ly peo-ple; let my love, Lord, bring rich-es to the poor. 2. Give me

lone - ly peo-ple; let my love, Lord, bring rich-es to the poor. 2. Give me

ah.

life, Lord, and make it tru - ly yours.

life, Lord, and make it tru - ly yours.

Anthems

THE BODY OF CHRIST IS BROKEN

Text: Michael Forster (b.1946)
Music: Rosalie Bonighton (b.1946)

lu – jah in the pre-sence of the ri – sen Lord!

lu – jah in the pre-sence of the ri – sen Lord!

We

join in com-me-mo-ra – tion of love's great tri – umph hour,

looking forward to peace and justice when the kingdom comes in loving pow'r. Sing hallelujah! Sing hallelujah! Sing hallelujah in the presence of the risen Lord!

373

THE GRAIL PRAYER

Text: Traditional Prayer
Music: Margaret Rizza (b.1929)

I give you my tongue to speak your words; I give you my mind, Lord, that you may think in me; I give you my spi - rit that you may pray in me, that you may pray in me.

mp

Lord

self that you may grow in me, so that it is you, Lord Je - sus, who

live and work and pray in me; I give you my whole self, that you may

live and work and pray in me. Lord

Je-sus, I give you my spi-rit, that you may

pray in me; I give you my heart, Lord, that you may

love in me, that you may love in me, pray in me,

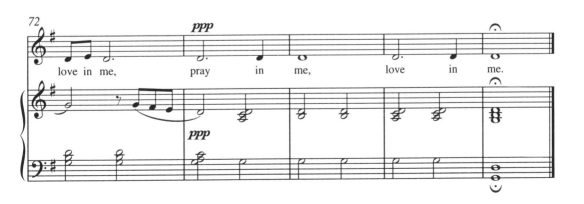

love in me, pray in me, love in me.

THE HEAVENS ARE TELLING

Text: Psalm 19:1-4
Music: Franz Joseph Haydn (1732-1809) arr. Colin Hand

The hea - vens are tel - ling the glo - ry of

The hea - vens are tel - ling the glo - ry of

God,

God,

the won-der of his work dis-plays the fir-ma-

the won-der of his work dis-plays the fir-ma-

ment,   the won-der of his

ment,   the won-der of his

work   dis - plays the fir-ma-ment.

work   dis - plays the fir-ma-ment.

work, the won-der of his work dis-plays the fir-ma-

work, the won-der of his work dis-plays the fir-ma-

ment, in all the lands re-sounds the

ment, in all the lands re-sounds the

word, ne-ver un-per-cei-ved, e-ver un-der-

word, ne-ver un-per-cei-ved, e-ver un-der-

Anthems

THE LORD COMES DOWN FROM HEAVEN

Text: Hubert J. Richards (b.1921) based on Psalm 33
Music: Andrew Moore (b.1954)

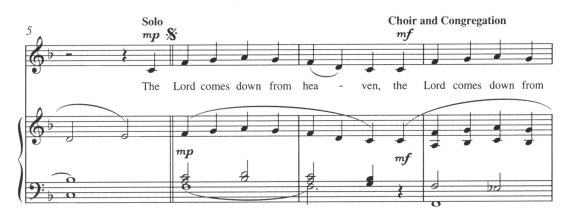

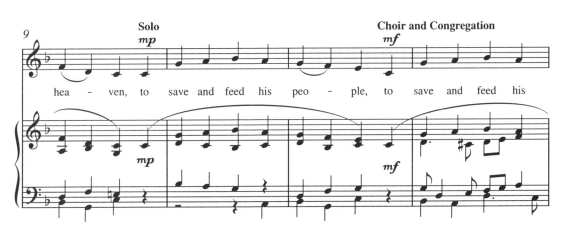

peo - ple. So raise up your eyes and re - joice.

Taste and see the good - ness of the Lord, the

Choir and Congregation

good-ness of the Lord. Taste and see the good - ness of the

Lord, the good - ness of the Lord.

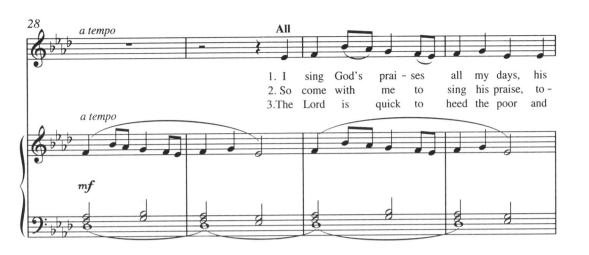

28

a tempo

All

1. I sing God's prai - ses all my days, his
2. So come with me to sing his praise, to -
3. The Lord is quick to heed the poor and

mf

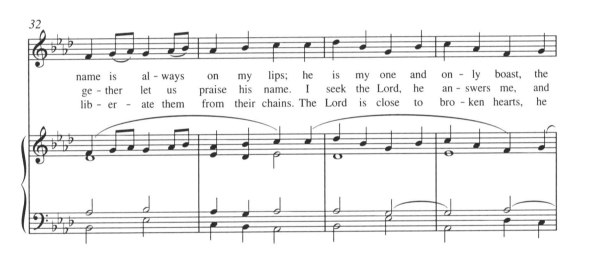

32

name is al - ways on my lips; he is my one and on - ly boast, the
ge - ther let us praise his name. I seek the Lord, he an - swers me, and
lib - er - ate them from their chains. The Lord is close to bro - ken hearts, he

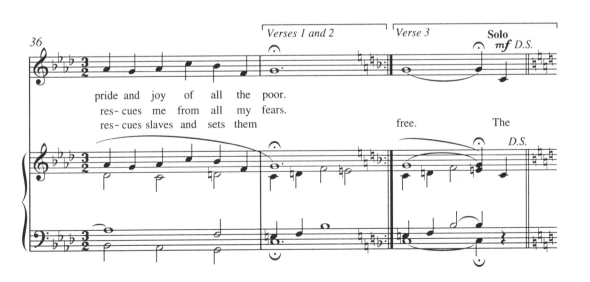

36

Verses 1 and 2 *Verse 3* **Solo** *mf* D.S.

pride and joy of all the poor.
res - cues me from all my fears.
res - cues slaves and sets them free. The

D.S.

391

THE SPIRIT LIVES TO SET US FREE

Text: Damian Lundy (1940-1997)
Music: Damian Lundy arr. Christopher Tambling (b.1964)

Sopranos and Altos

Walk in the light, walk in the light, walk

in the light, walk in the light of the Lord.

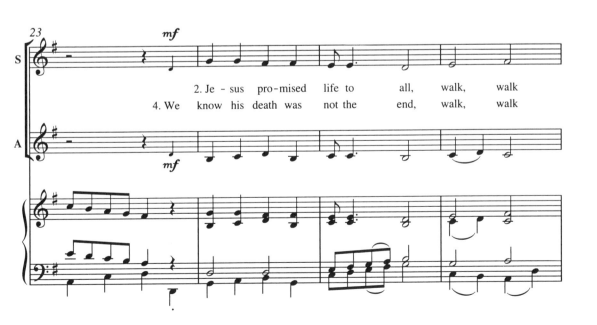

mf

2. Je - sus pro - mised life to all, walk, walk
4. We know his death was not the end, walk, walk

mf

27

in the light. The dead were wa - kened by his call, walk, walk
in the light. He gave his Spi- rit to be our friend, walk, walk

31

in the light. Walk in the light, walk
in the light.

35

in the light, walk in the light, walk in the light of the

Lord. 3. He died in pain on Cal - va - ry, walk, walk
5. By Je - sus' love our wounds are healed, walk, walk

in the light, to save the lost like you and me, walk, walk
in the light. The Fa - ther's kind - ness is re - vealed, walk, walk

in the light.
in the light. Walk in the light, walk in the light,

walk   in the light,   walk in the light of the Lord.   Lord.

mf

Man.

Sopranos and Altos

f

cresc.

ff

Ped.

6. The

Spi - rit lives in   you and   me,   walk,   walk   in the light. His

f

TO BE IN YOUR PRESENCE

Text and Music: Noel Richards
arr. Christopher Tambling

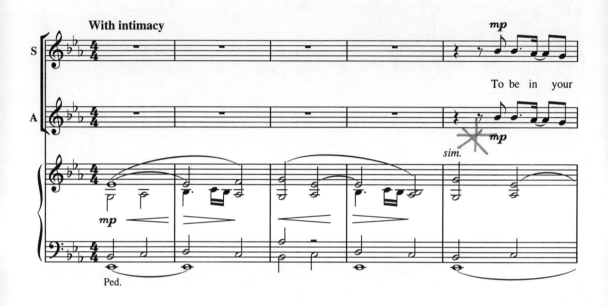

VENI, LUMEN CORDIUM

Text: Stephen Langton (d.1228)
Music: Margaret Rizza (b.1929)

Translation: *Come, light of our hearts. Come, Holy Spirit, come.*

WAKE UP, O PEOPLE

Text: Marie Lydia Pereira (b.1920) from Romans 13:11-14
Music: Marie Lydia Pereira arr. Christopher Tambling

His glo-ry will ap-pear. Wake up!

Your hour of grace is near-er

than it e-ver was.

Lord.

2. The night of sin has passed. Wake up!
   The light is near at last. Wake up!
   The day star, Christ, the Son of God, will soon appear.

3. To live in love and peace. Wake up!
   To let all quarrels cease. Wake up!
   To live that all you do may stand the light of day.

4. That Christ may be your shield. Wake up!
   That death to life may yield. Wake up!
   That heaven's gate be opened wide again for you.

WE ARE HIS PEOPLE

Text: Susan Sayers (b.1946) based on Psalm 99
Music: Andrew Moore (b.1954)

11

D.C.

Come and ga - ther be - fore him now, sing - ing songs of glad - ness.

2. Understand that the Lord is our God;
   he it is who made us.
   We, his people, belong to him,
   he our loving shepherd.

3. O how faithful and good is the Lord,
   loving us for ever;
   rich in mercy and faithfulness,
   true through all the ages.

WHAT KIND OF MAN WAS THIS

Text: Michael Forster (b.1946)
Music: Christopher Tambling (b.1964)

way of truth, all o-ther things a-bove? What kind of
to his side, and gave us all a place? What kind of

man was this, what kind of love? 2. What kind of
man was this, what kind of grace? 3. What kind of

man was this, who o-pened up his heart to those who

sought to tear his flesh a-part; whose all-for-

giv - ing words his per - fect na - ture prove?. What kind of

man was this, what kind of love? 4. What kind of

Optional Descant for Voices or Instrument

Ah, ah,

man was this, who helped us all to see the full - ness

of our hu - man dig - ni - ty; so hope - ful

ah, ah,

in des - pair, so no - ble in dis - grace? What kind of

man was this, what kind of grace?

ah.

For Barry Rose and the choristers of St Albans Abbey

WHEN I SURVEY THE WONDROUS CROSS

Text: Isaac Watts (1674-1748)
Music: Malcolm Archer (b.1952)

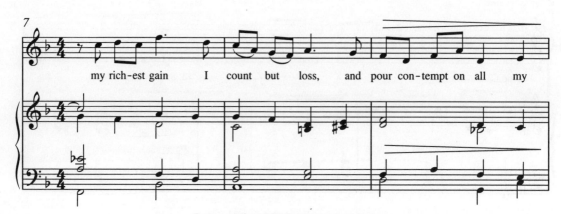

pride.

All *mf*

2. For-bid it, Lord, that

I should boast, save in the cross of Christ, my God:

all the vain things that charm me most, I sac-ri-fice them to his

blood.

p

3. See from his head, his

hands, his feet, sor - row and love flow ming - ling down:

S: did e'er such love and sor - row meet, or thorns com - pose so rich a

A: did e'er such love and sor - row meet, or thorns com - pose so rich a

Optional Descant

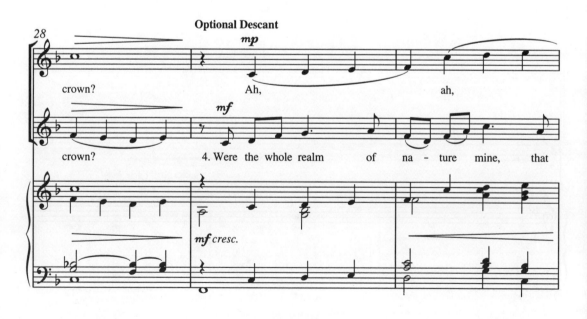

crown? Ah, ah,

crown? 4. Were the whole realm of na - ture mine, that

WONDERFUL YOUR DEEDS, LORD

Text: Edwin Le Grice (1911-1992)
Music: Adrian Vernon Fish (b.1956)

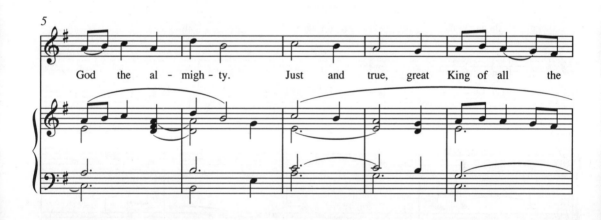

glo - ry here dis - plays. To the one who reigns in

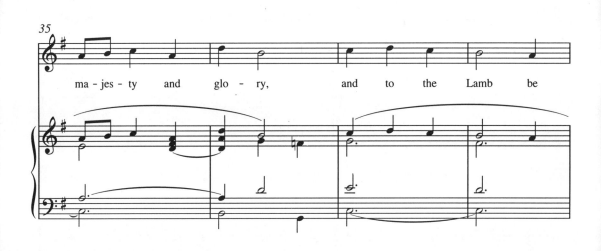

ma - jes - ty and glo - ry, and to the Lamb be

e - ver - last - ing praise.

YOU ARE THE CENTRE

Text and Music: Margaret Rizza (b.1929)

You are the cen - tre, you are my life, you are the

cen - tre, O Lord, of my life. Come, Lord, and guide me,

ZADOK THE PRIEST

Text: from Scripture
Music: George Frideric Handel (1685-1759) arr. Colin Hand

So - lo- mon King.

So - lo- mon King.

Allegro

And all the peo - ple re - joic'd, re -

And all the peo - ple re - joic'd, re -

joic'd, re - joic'd, and all the peo - ple re -

joic'd, re - joic'd, and all the peo - ple re -

peo - ple re - joic'd,   re -

peo - ple re - joic'd,   re -

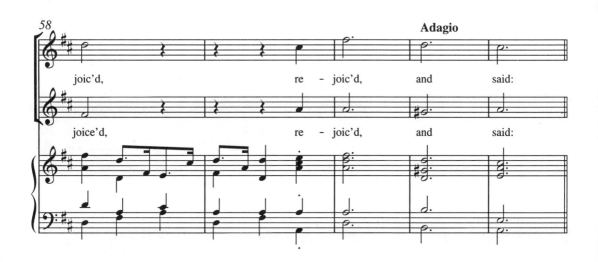

Adagio

joic'd,   re - joic'd,   and   said:

joice'd,   re - joic'd,   and   said:

A tempo ordinario

_ff_

God save the King!   Long live the King!   God save the King!

_ff_   _f_

God save the King!   Long live the King!   God save the King!   May the King live   for

God save the King! Long live the King! May the King live for e - ver, a-men,

God save the King! Long live the King! a-men,

Ped. Man.

a-men, al - le - lu - ia, al - le - lu - ia, a - men, a - - -

a-men, al - le - lu - ia, al - le - lu - ia, a - men, a - - -

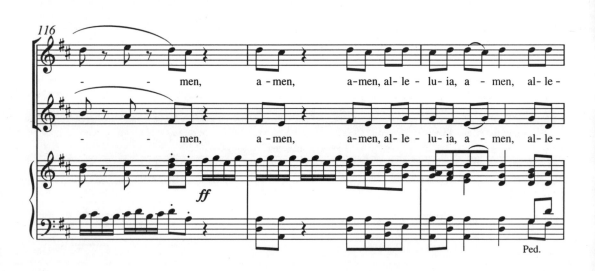